I lost my trees.
I lost my silver moons.

—Langston Hughes

BiG TOWN

a novel of Africville

STEPHENS GERARD MALONE

Vagrant Press is an imprint of
Nimbus Publishing Limited
3731 Mackintosh St, Halifax, NS B3K 5A5
(902) 455-4286 nimbus.ca

Printed and bound in Canada

Author photo: David Parker
Cover design: Heather Bryan

This novel is a work of fiction. Names, characters, places, and incidents are either the product of the author's imagination or are used fictitiously.

The author acknowledges the support of the Province of Nova Scotia through the Department of Communities, Culture and Heritage.

Nimbus Publishing acknowledges the financial support for its publishing activities from the Government of Canada through the Canada Book Fund (CBF) and the Canada Council for the Arts, and from the Province of Nova Scotia through the Department of Communities, Culture and Heritage.

Africville was a Negro "enclave" within the city of Halifax, inhabited by approximately four hundred people comprising eighty families, many of whom were descended from settlers who had moved there over a century ago. Tucked away in a corner of the city, relatively invisible, thought of as a "shack town", Africville was a depressed neighbourhood or "community" both in physical terms and in socio-economic indicators. Its dwellings were located beside the City dump, and railroad tracks cut across the one unpaved dirt road leading into the area. Sewerage, lighting, and other public services were conspicuously absent. The people had little education, very low income, and were much underemployed. Property claims were in chaos. Only a handful of families could establish legal title; others claimed squatter rights; and still others rented. Africville, long a black mark against society, had been designated for future industrial and harbour development. Many observers reported that despite these liabilities there was a strong sense of "community" and that some residents expressed satisfaction with living in Africville.

Donald H. Clairmont and Dennis W. Magill
Africville Relocation Report, 1971

SIX DOWN, ONE ACROSS. MARKS SCRATCHED ON the shed with a piece of chalk. Early stepped back, smiled. Six down, one across meant hallelujah day. No crawling under cars at Mr. Welford's garage, no wearing out memories, and best of all, his pops too hungover to see him go. Not far, and not for good. Early just wanted to watch the morning train cut by houses sprinkled across the tracks, thick like spring flowers: blue, yellow, even pink—only houses didn't get picked.

Buddy riding the engine up front, Mr. Young, who wasn't young at all, hollered, "That you down there, Early?"

Early ran alongside and waved back. "Sure is, where you headin'?"

"Maybe Truro, maybe the moon"—and Early laughed.

Horse got killed once by that train. And those boys of Mrs. Aada's, but she didn't talk about them anymore.

Greening birch and dogwood by the tracks looked ready for new leaves to pop out, and peepers had started giving the cheep cheep in the ponds. Real sparkly on the harbour too. After the click-click click-click click-click of the train passed, the singing from the church took over from the birds, then feet stomping, and Mrs. Aada played on the piano. Early wished his pops'd let him pray to God like those Baptists.

He scratched the dog waiting by the steps and said look, Ol' Nip, even that cargo ship is tryin' to catch a listen—as it sliced through flat water without a sound or a ripple on the way through the Narrows.

Wade in the water, children.

Wade in the water.

Sure was nothing finer than a wade in the water.

Mrs. Etta Briscoe in a flowered pillbox hat and white gloves stuck her head out the door. She didn't look too happy to see Early or the dog. Toby said Mrs. Briscoe, come Judgment Day, probably'd say Jesus looked to need a haircut.

"Early Okander, if you're going to start that caterwauling, then get inside and let the good Lord hear."

Early wanted nothing better than to be in there sitting beside Toby, but he said, "Missus, you know my pops won't let me in this nigger church."

When the singing was done and the preaching finished, Early helped get Ol' Nip away from the doors, seeing as how he was pretty old and didn't move so fast. Toby and his grandpa, Aubrey, were the last ones to come out. Ol' Nip tried to jump up for a pat, but didn't get very far.

Mrs. Aada put her gloves back on. "Heard you singing

again, Early. What did I tell you about making that racket?"

Early knew she wanted to make Aubrey husband number three. Too bad. Aubrey liked the singing lady he was always writing letters to.

When Toby saw Early, he got an ear-to-ear smile, ran over, and climbed onto Early's back.

Woof woof, some kid said, like Toby's got a pet dog other than Ol' Nip. The kid's folks took his arm and swung him around with something about hushing his mouth.

"You're too big for him to carry you," Aubrey said.

No sir. Early didn't feel Toby one bit.

Mrs. Aada supposed that Early was inviting himself around for breakfast like he did every Sunday. Mrs. Aada always cooked after church and she expected big appetites. Eggs in butter, apple sausages, lots of toast—even fresh milk from Mrs. Trilby, the cow she kept in her backyard. Early's favourite was blueberry pancakes. Mrs. Aada made those when he picked a bowl full of berries by the train tracks, except that wasn't until summer. Early could eat blueberries 'til they came out his ears.

Early and Toby went to see after Mrs. Trilby. Hey, you're pulling those teats right well, Early. Then Early washed in a barrel of water because Toby reminded him.

Aubrey and the boys ate in Mrs. Aada's kitchen; the grocery store for folks in Africville took up her front room. Mrs. Aada sold Early Cherry Blossoms in there if he got tips. Spare cash he was supposed to keep—just between you and me, boy—from those men who played cards on

Saturday nights with Pops. Early loved Cherry Blossoms. Toby loved Cherry Blossoms. Toby'd suck out the candied fruit in the middle and save the chocolate shell for Early. That was like getting an extra one.

Aubrey took a seat at the table with Ol' Nip curled on the floor beside him. "You know, must be the Lord's day," he said. "Can't smell the dump—like it's Good Friday. Always grey on that sad day and always sweet smelling on Sunday."

Mrs. Aada was pretty sure Jesus got more important work to do than fiddling with the weather. She set out her best china and got to stirring and chopping while the bacon crackled. Her singing was so Aubrey wouldn't try to argue with her.

The hallelujahs carried on like maybe Mrs. Aada forgot church was over, except she was in her kitchen filling plates. Growing boys got to eat. Aubrey said if Early grew any more, he wouldn't be able to get through doors. When the old folks weren't watching, Toby scraped his plate onto Early's, because Early carried him around on his back, or on his shoulders.

When Mrs. Aada started making lovey-dovey eyes at Aubrey, Toby pinched Early, so Early asked if the old man wanted anything at the hardware store.

But Mrs. Aada said, "You're not pulling the wool over my eyes. Hardware store?" Why Aubrey let those boys go picking in garbage, putting Early to work like that when Aubrey's own place needed fixing, was what she wanted to know. Damn fool, she called him.

There was good stuff in the dump, Missus, and it was called scavenging. Early found a pair of ice skates once. Imagine, someone throwing them out. They fit Toby then, too small now. Anyhow, it didn't matter 'cause the snow was gone. Early and his pops scavenged all the time. Got good money for car parts if they were still working or at least looked like they might. Finding those kinds of things made his pops real happy. Said Early shouldn't be carting stuff out of the dump just to give away when there was good money to be made. That was how Early found the lamp he fixed so Mrs. Aada could sew better and not have to get new glasses in Halifax. Mrs. Aada paid Early and Toby a Cherry Blossom for that.

Outside, Early took his shirt off and put Toby on instead. Standing on the church grass was Mrs. Etta Briscoe. Chatting with her was Deacon English. He had a tree in his yard that got eaten alive by caterpillars every summer. He waved, but not that Mrs. Briscoe.

"Hey, fellas. Going swimming?"

"Yes, sir."

Mrs. Briscoe said Early wasn't decent and what was Aubrey thinking, letting Toby go around with him like that. Maybe talking to Deacon English, she thought that Toby and Early couldn't hear, but they heard her just the same. From up top, Toby said he was sticking his tongue out at her because he knew Early wouldn't, those words of hers going in one ear and out his other.

Must have rained last night because of all the puddles on the dirt road. Toby made a game. If Early stepped in one, he owed Toby a Coke. Early had no money left for Cokes, so he had to jump around. Toby almost slipped off his shoulders and fell backwards. Got a right laugh about that.

"How are your chickens?"

Early stopped jumping.

"Start makin' eggs soon, Pops says."

Some fella owing money gave the chicks to D Jay. First time they tried to raise chickens. Mr. Sumlar complained about the noise, and said raccoons were trouble enough without them sniffing around after the chickens. Early gave them all names: Maud, Evelyn, Flora, Libby, Mercy, and his favourite because she was white like a seagull, Emily. Mrs. Aada said you couldn't give chickens people names, but Early didn't care. Next to Toby, they were his best friends because they didn't mind what went on in that shed come Saturday nights, but that was just for him to know.

"Let's see if they made some after."

They were pretty much 'round the turn. Train tracks on one side, Bedford Basin on the other. Aubrey said that the trains coming through Africville used to burn coal, and his old man collected the chunks that fell off. Burning that coal kept the frost away in winter. But that was when times were tough, he said. Trains were diesel now, but Early figured just as noisy.

Not too much of a stink coming off the dump, smouldering nearby. Sunday made things quiet, although they saw Tom Reed and his buddy, Charlie Savage, skipping along the tracks. Probably been over at the dump stoning rats. They only made faces at Toby and Early as if they'd swallowed a canary. Mrs. Aada said that a lot, about swallowing canaries.

"Still there?"

Their raft sure was, but there'd be no telling Aubrey. He'd get angry if Toby got wet, maybe catch a cold. Early couldn't say no to Toby, though. Being out on the harbour was his favourite thing to do.

Good thing the raft was pulled up from the shore where Early left it. Toby got down from his perch and they scrambled aboard. At first it was tippy, then Early got it right and poled away from the shore. Toby lay down and put his hand in the water, started singing. Made songs up. Some got words, some didn't. Toby said that was how they came to him. Early didn't hear songs unless they were on the radio or the TV, or when Molasses Jack rattled off a reel with his spoons.

"Let's float down to Tibby's Pond, maybe even to the dock and see if there's a ship."

Toby was good at planning things, and Early didn't mind paddling, taking them along the shore road that came down off Barrington Street with the train tracks running alongside. Aubrey called it Campbell Road, and said one day it was going to be paved with streetlights just like in the city. Early, he liked to say, that special project they're building by Mrs. Trilby's pen is going to see to that.

Used to be a school next door to the whitewashed church with the red roof. Now Toby's got to walk pretty far. He didn't mind going to the Richmond School, when he wasn't too sick, but it was hard going up those hills knotted with stands of alder and birch, some maple, everything swelling into leaf, just to find out there was a city back of all that. Couldn't see it from here, and when Early slept outside by the shore like he did sometimes, there was no hearing it. Just frogs making air and ducks shaking water out their feathers.

Toby pointed to where winter tore off some shingles from Aubrey's place, right next door to Mrs. Aada and near where the boys went swimming in Tibby's Pond. Aubrey's house was small, got smaller when Toby's mom, Deborah, came by, but then even a bigger place like Mrs. Aada's would be too small for her. Good thing Deborah never stayed long.

Early didn't care much for Toby's mom. Pretty woman, but a hellcat for sure. Could turn right fast. Got mad when Early said he didn't have two bucks to buy her smokes. She knew Early's dad sent those men out to see him in the chicken shed, and what for. Early was as nice as pie to Deborah, so maybe she wouldn't ask how come he gave all his money from fixing Mr. Welford's cars to his pops and not take Deborah out drinking? Early never drank. No way, not unless his pops held his mouth open and poured it down.

Toby pointed to the boys kicking around a ball in Kildare's Field and said looks like they're getting up a game. Sometimes Early got asked to play because he could hit the ball out of the field, but mostly he didn't like to since Toby couldn't.

"Where's Dartmouth?"

Early pointed.

"Where's Bedford?"

Early pointed again, further, across the water. Toby was happy that Early got it right.

"You think there's pirates out there?"

Toby didn't think so. At least, not in Nova Scotia.

Good. D Jay kept saying he was going to sell Early to the next band of pirates coming through, so he could wash his hands of him. Ha. Ha.

"If there's no pirates, let's get your grandpa out here, see his house from the water."

"Naw. He won't come."

Maybe because of Aubrey's wooden leg. Not a whole one, just wood below the knee on his left side. Got that in the war. Same war that killed Aubrey's dad when those ships went head on in the harbour. The old fella was watering his window geranium. Mostly the folks up in Richmond got it, not much broken in Africville, unless you count Aubrey's pa. Aubrey was somewhere in Europe getting his leg blown to pieces, came home to find most of the city looking like a book of matches gone off at once. Didn't notice that leg so much now. Aubrey walked regular, like that wooden part wasn't there. Said it didn't hurt neither, but sometimes the memory of what it was like came back, then it was awfully sore.

"Hey."

They'd gone out too far. D Jay had said, Early, one day you'll be walking on the tracks, head in the clouds, bang. Problem solved.

The raft started to break up. Early stroked fast after noticing, but Toby laughed and didn't mind getting dunked. The harbour water was still cold. He might catch a chill. Early got him back to shore as the raft split in two.

"Thought you built this good."

Early thought so too. Someone left some real fine wood down at the dump. Sometimes, a whole house got left there, in pieces, not like they dropped it off whole. This wood was good, and Early made sure it was nailed proper in the raft. So after Early got Toby back on shore, he turned over the raft and had a look.

"That cross piece is gone."

"I saw you put that on. You think it fell off?"

That was a mystery.

"Bet that's what Tom and Charlie were doing out this way."

"Guess no raftin'."

"Can't you fix it?"

"Maybe I can get another piece of wood from the dump."

Toby wanted to go, but all this fuss with the raft wore out his breathing.

"I won't be long. You'll see."

Handy having a dump next door. Gotta be careful picking though. Early knew there was sometimes a fire burning underneath and you could get scorched because folks threw out oil and gas from their cars. Other bits too, made you cough, and your eyes burned if you got too close. Then there were the broken cups and plates and needle bits of wood. Steel, that was the worst on bare feet. Had to be some careful picking your way around so you didn't get cut. Early did that once. Couldn't work for a week. D Jay took a stick to the part of him that wasn't bleeding. Good thing Toby was waiting back at the raft. He had bare feet too.

"Sweet Jesus."

The things people put here in the dump. A perfectly good church door, all shiny except where the fires got it a bit black, with a window of coloured glass. Wait till Aubrey saw this.

Early held the door over his head so it didn't get any more scratched, but a door wasn't easy to cart out of the dump when you got your eyes down around your feet.

"Early, that's too big."

Sometimes Early forgot what he was about and moved his head on to something else, like remembering Aubrey saying that if he saw a door in the dump he was to bring it back. Always had a need for a good door. So when Toby got all quiet Early figured he was thinking that carrying the door meant no more rafting today. But Toby was just watching a girl up on the road watching them.

She wore a pair of shorts and a dirty white T-shirt. Buckle-up plastic sandals on her feet. Early'd never seen her before. Pieces of stringy brown hair loose from her ponytail hung down over her eyes. She was sitting on a pink bicycle, moving it back and forth between her legs. Neither Toby nor Early ever saw a pink one before, especially one with a white basket and rainbow tassels hanging from the handlebars. The girl had a camera hanging around her neck and she sure liked to stare.

"What's your name?"

"Penny."

She tried hard not to look at Toby.

"Hey, Penny."

"Who's that?" She meant Early.

"He's my best friend."

Penny giggled. "He's too big."

"No he's not."

"How old are you?"

"Tell her, Early."

He flashed his hand three times, then held up two fingers.

Penny said it was old, even older than her brother, Derek. "He's sixteen and collects *Monster* magazines. I sneak into his room and read them. What school you go to?"

"Richmond."

Penny's eyes got thin. "How come I've never seen you there?"

"Dunno."

"You must be in the slow learner class."

"Am not. Early's the slow learner."

That's because letters and numbers ran all over the page when he went to school. But not Toby. He liked to read those books his mom left about people in fine houses who talked funny.

"He's retarded?"

Toby said it was because Early's dad made his mom drink stuff from a car battery when he was getting born.

"Nice bike you got there."

Penny gripped the handlebars.

"No one's gonna steal it."

"My mother says we can't leave anything good outside or it gets stolen. That's 'cause we live next door to that slum over there and Negroes are always stealing."

Early wanted to know what a slum was.

Penny nodded towards the church. "It's where poor people live."

"Toby lives over there. He's not poor."

"Well, my mom says so."

Toby asked Penny where she lived.

Turning around awkwardly, not letting go of the handlebar, she pointed to a row of houses behind the train tracks. If pickings were slim in the dump, D Jay'd send Early up there with a squeaky three-wheel shopping cart. Lots of good stuff got put to the curb on garbage days, like that tube of coloured teardrops held together with brass. Hanging it from the roof of Aubrey's shed with a light inside sure would have made him happy. But some old man in shorts, watering his grass, had hosed Early down and run him off.

"Must have been Mr. Londsberry. He hosed down cats too. Used to have this barky little dog that pooped all over the grass between the road and the sidewalk. My mom said someone was going to get their shoes dirty in all that poo and there was a law about picking it up, so she kept phoning and writing and getting everyone to sign things until the city came and took the dog."

Early wondered if the man felt sad when his dog was taken away.

"Naw, Mr. Londsberry died right after anyway, so it was a good thing."

"Where do you live?"

"The yellow house."

Early thought it looked funny.

"Is not."

"Can I ride your bike?"

"No, Early, you're too big. You'll break it, and anyhow, it's for a girl."

"Is not."

"Yes it is."

Penny shoved her bike to the ground.

"Okay, see if I care. I hope he does break it. Never wanted a girl's bike anyhow."

She stood there, staring, with her arms folded. Then she slid down the embankment towards them, the buckles on her plastic shoes rattling, that camera bouncing off her chest.

"Wanna see my pet snail?"

She pulled a glass Aspirin bottle from her pocket.

Early asked, "What does it eat?"

"Lettuce."

"Looks lonely in there."

"I poked a hole in the top so it can breathe. Here, you can hold it."

Toby didn't get far doing that because Penny grabbed her snail back. "Eeew! What's wrong with your arm?"

Toby tugged his sleeve over his peeling skin.

"C'mon, Early, let's go."

Toby must have forgot all about that snail.

"Where you guys going?"

"To our raft. Early's going to fix it so we can go on the water."

"Me too?"

"What for?"

"Need a picture. See? With my brother's camera. He got it for Christmas, but it only took pictures of his foot when he put the film in."

"What do you want a picture of?"

"Can't tell."

"It's our raft, you have to."

"Yeah," Early added. "It's ours."

Penny thought about it.

"Can you keep a secret?"

Early and Toby nodded, but Early knew secrets had a way of getting away from him.

"There's an elephant in the harbour, and the newspaper'll give anyone twenty-five dollars for a picture."

Early whistled. That was a lot.

"And I'm getting that picture."

"What'll you do with all the money?"

"Buy a ten-speed. I hate that girly thing up there. I wanted Santa to bring me one like Derek's. He's got a racing bike, and he's too big for it, but he never lets me ride it. Mom says that one's better for girls. So, can I come on your raft?"

"If there's elephants under the water, how can they get air? And the ships'd hit 'em."

Penny thought so too, but she pulled a crumpled piece of newspaper from her back pocket and handed it to Early.

"See for yourself. If it's in the paper, it's gotta be so."

"I don't read too good. Here, Toby."

"Can he read?"

"Yes I can," said Toby, "and hey, stupid, it says someone saw a sea elephant in the harbour. That's what they want the picture of."

"Yeah, a type of elephant."

"That's just a dirty ol' seal."

"Me and Toby sees them all the time."

Penny grabbed back her piece of paper. "What do you know, you're just a bunch of bozos."

She crawled up to the road and got back on the bike. Made short work of putting the train tracks between her and them.

"Better get that door to Grandpa."

On the way home, Early carried the door instead of Toby on his back. Charlie Savage was waiting on the steps of the church as they came by and he threw rocks. Early didn't want Toby to get hit, so he used the door as a shield. Too bad that stone broke the window.

THE RAIN WAS SURE COMING DOWN HARD. EARLY
heard the wind, then, like someone throwing buckets of
water against the trailer. City was getting hit with what
his pops called a real pisser, and their trailer leaked. Came
in from the roof. When it was windy, the place could really
get to rocking.

"Early, you lazy piece of ass, you get the tarpaulin on?"

Oh no. Forgot.

"Jesus fuckin' Mary!"

D Jay said that when he got mad. Said Early had half a
brain and didn't know anything because of his old lady.

"Get out there, and get that tarp on the roof."

The tattered piece of oiled canvas had blown most
of the way down to the harbour. Early made too much
noise getting up on the trailer because even though it
was blowing hard, D Jay was banging the roof inside and
telling Early to keep the fuck quiet. It took a while to get
that tarpaulin up there and all smoothed out in the wind,

weighted down with old tires from the dump. Early was soaked to the skin when he got back inside.

Pops had put the table down and folded back one of the seats to make their bed. Not much room for sleeping, Early being so big. That's why he slept with the chickens on Saturday nights when D Jay's buddies came over for cards and drinking.

"Hurry up and get those clothes off. Hang 'em up to dry."

D Jay didn't want Early to get sick and not go in to work for Mr. Welford at the garage. Lose a day's wages if he did.

"You naked there, boy?"

"Yes, sir."

"Then c'mere."

Day after the rain, sun coming out, folks had their laundry flapping on lines. The kind of day that even dried out wet eyes. It was a long walk to Mr. Welford's garage. Early was hungry, but in a few more weeks there'd be all kinds of berries to eat on the way, and he'd be getting to Mr. Welford's with a full belly.

Early walked along the tracks, then took the road through Africville. Not too many folks around at this hour, except for the garbage trucks. Those fellas driving into the dump weren't so rough. Here you go, Early, day old bread someone was throwing out, don't mind the mould, ha ha, it's good for you, it's called penicillin. Maybe even some tins of canned meat'd come his way.

Sometimes Early found really good stuff just lying there on the way to work. Once he found a half-empty bottle of Coke. The fizz was all gone, but it tasted good just the same. Found a key chain too. Didn't have any keys, but Early kept it in his pocket. You never know, Early, Ben at Mr. Welford's said when he showed him, one day you might have something worth locking.

Ben was older than D Jay, maybe even older than Aubrey. He'd worked at the garage for so long, he said they used to shoe horses. Early thought Ben must be having fun with him over saying that, horses wearing shoes. When they first met, Ben said, Early, you call me Ben. No mister for him. So Ben showed Early where to hang his coat and how to clean his tools when Early first came to work for Mr. Welford. Ben had grown boys of his own in the navy, and he was proud of them even if they didn't visit much anymore. Said Early was a right natural mechanic for someone who didn't read so well. Glad to have you aboard, son. On that first day when he saw Early didn't have anything to eat for lunch, he offered half his sandwich. Ben's missus, she packed one for Early every day now.

Early was smiling, thinking of two thick slices of bread missus made herself, with big chunks of grain Early liked to pick out and have a look at. Sometimes there'd be cheese, against each side of ham or turkey. Maybe a pickle. Thinking about being in Ben's kitchen, watching his missus make that sandwich for him was so fine, Early almost missed seeing the nicest shade of blue he'd ever seen, except on blue jays, on their head and on their backs. Only this blue wasn't on a bird. A five-dollar bill just waiting for him to pick it up. Right there on the sidewalk on the way into town as if someone said, you wait there, five dollars, until Early Okander comes by. He stared at it for a long time, thinking it couldn't be real. Ran the rest of the way to Mr. Welford's so he could show Ben.

"Early, you've won the lottery. What are you gonna do with all the cash, son?"

Early couldn't say.

Mr. Welford, working in one of the bays, yelled over, it looked like Early for once could get his own lunch, seeing as how he was rich now.

"Good idea," Ben said. "How about having your lunch in a restaurant?"

Seeing as how Early'd never been to one, Ben offered to take him.

They were like a couple of kittens that morning, joking around about what they were going to order, maybe a turkey, maybe two whole turkeys, maybe two whole turkeys with ice cream on top. Even Mr. Welford got into the fun.

"Ladies, sounds like you two have a date."

They laughed at that, mostly Early, because they weren't ladies. Then Mr. Welford tossed some keys to Ben to go pick up those new tires.

"And you might as well get yourselves off to lunch before that money burns a hole in Early's pocket."

He and Ben drove to Quinpool Road and took a window booth at the Ardmore Tea Room. Ben knew the place, brought his missus there a lot. Good food, real cheap.

"Early, you order the hot chicken sandwich and some pie."

They both did. And Cokes. Still fizzy. The waitress brought a plate with biscuits and butter. Almost as good as Mrs. Aada's. Early thought he might explode from eating so much. Ben laughed. Said he wished he could do this with his boys, but he didn't even know where their ship was. Early thought about doing this with his pops.

"You still living down in Africville?" Ben tore open his biscuit, put on lots of butter.

Early smiled.

"No offence, but you know what I say about that place. Not right for a boy like you. And I know. Been there during the war. Only place in Halifax a sailor could get to drink, game a cards if you'd a mind for it. Things are different now. Not right a man having a son like you down there. City's going to clean those squatters out, you hear me, Early? Should've done that years ago."

After lunch, Early walked up to the girl at the cash register like Ben told him to do and gave her the money. She smiled and said thank you very much, hon, and gave him change back.

"That piece of rhubarb pie, ma'am, was the best I ever had. I got money left over to get another piece all wrapped up to take home?"

Ben laughed. "Early, you got a hollow leg if you still want more."

That extra piece of pie wasn't for him. It was for D Jay. Not right Pops should miss out on Early being so favoured. And the only man Early knew who had a fake leg was Aubrey, but he didn't think it was hollow, just made of wood.

Ben told him he was a dumb kid, but he was smiling.

Another five-dollar bill wasn't waiting for Early on the way home, just a bicycle lying in the bushes by the train tracks. White basket bent up in the corner and one of those tassels hanging from the handlebars was missing. The girl looking for the elephants would be upset when she found out it was gone. She lived on the hilltop. Early remembered that fat guy up there in shorts running after him with the hose. Not right leaving the bike in the bushes though, even if it was pink and the girl didn't like it. Someone was sure to help themselves.

Early had to do some backtracking. Not along the train tracks in behind the church that ran along the waterfront, but the upper tracks. The ones to the old cotton mill that wound up the hill past those houses where that girl lived. Trains used to run by the slaughterhouse where they cut up pigs. The incinerator burned garbage around there now. Early put his arm over his nose and wondered if it stunk this bad in Rockhead Prison, over the other way. Mrs. Aada said there even used to be a hospital up there for folks so sick they had to keep them by themselves so other people didn't catch things. That was gone now too, but Mrs. Aada said Halifax could always find something good to stick by Africville.

That girl was lucky. Paved roads where she lived. Early figured they didn't get bumpy rides in the spring when melting snow washed out the Africville road. And the houses. Big, with big wide lawns. Her house, the yellow one, was the third in on the side of the street overlooking the harbour. Even had a train running through the backyard. And her house looked special. All the others on her side of the road had verandas on the back. But not hers. Her porch was by the driveway, so you could watch the cars coming and going. Nice grass. Had a sprinkler that went hiss hiss hiss.

The driveway was empty and no one was around the house, so Early figured he'd lay the bike against the side wall and get over to see Toby, because Toby was probably wondering why Early was late coming from Mr. Welford's.

"Whatcha doing?"

The house next door had storm windows and a kid had her head sideways underneath so she could talk through the vent holes along the bottom of the frame. Behind her, Early heard a dog barking.

"You stealing Penny's bike?"

"No, bringin' it back."

"Mrs. Deforest, some guy's taking Penny's bike!"

A woman pushing herself out the door on a metal stand, scraped against the decking. What did Early think he was doing? The words were shaky and the woman spit all over the place, right down her front. Her chest sagged like Mrs.

Aada's, and the back of her dress was hiked up into her underpants.

The girl in the window called for her mom.

Early didn't wait around. Sounded like that yappy dog was going to get him no matter how fast he ran. Then it stopped. The dog was tied to the clothesline and didn't know it was at the end till it choked quiet.

When Early stopped to catch his breath, his chest felt sticky. That piece of pie in his shirt pocket had got squished.

EARLY CLIMBED ON TOP OF THE TRAILER. D JAY wanted more tires up there to keep the tarpaulin in place. Not so easy to do on one of those Nova Scotia days when May cloud and wind came right out of nowhere, made you think, hey, what the hell happened to spring?

Early liked their trailer because it was painted red. Used to be red before the rust set in. Real tiny inside. That was why he slept with the chickens on Saturday nights. In the summer the trailer got real hot inside, no more than a metal box, so Early took his blanket and slept under the stars. Slept better, too, because if he wet the bed inside, D Jay'd rub his nose in the mess. Said it was how you learned a dog, so why not Early? But outside in the winter, got real cold. Put in a woodstove a few years back, but D Jay said no fires till November, and no fires after April. Wood was too dear. But Early's pops made him take wood from the neighbours when they were sleeping. Said he was owed that, so Early shouldn't mind doing it.

From up on the trailer Early could see the white lambs on the pockets of Penny's woollen sweater. The girl sure didn't like riding her bike. Throwing it down, the bell tinkled. She sat and crossed her legs, giving the trailer a once over.

"Hey, up there. You live here?"

"Me and Pops."

Except that Early's dad got work at Pier 9, hauling freight off and on those ships. He was gone for a few days when that happened. Said he was owed a lot more hours than what he got, and what he got paid for. Fuckin' good for nothin' union. Lucky thing the girl came back when she did, walking her pink bike along the train tracks, D Jay not being around.

"How come you don't live over by the church?"

"Pops says we're close enough to Coonville."

"Pretty small to live in, that trailer." The girl pointed at the hut with the pointed roof. "That where you go to the bathroom?"

Early said used to be taking a leak meant using the bushes outside. But when D Jay saw Early being good with his hands, he said a man ought to have a bit of privacy when he takes a shit. So he made Early dig a hole and build a shitter. It had a window out back to let in the light and you didn't get wet in there when it rained.

Only thing, the hole filled up. D Jay told Early, you got to dig a new one. How big? Big enough to stand in. But if he did that, how did he get out? Get yourself a ladder, you retard, and climb out. But Pops, how do I get out to get the ladder? That got D Jay mad, said Early was disrespecting him with foolishness.

D Jay came at him with a bat that day, saying those gophers that got run over on the road got more brains, and Early could thank his slut of a mother for that. Woman didn't care who she drank with, so D Jay was right to put battery acid in her shine. Only that made her baby come early. D Jay figured the kid and his mom wouldn't be around long enough for her to get Early a real name, so why bother? Early's mom flopped around on a bed for a long time, but nobody could make out her words.

Early was some sore after getting beat. Couldn't use his arm for a long time. Couldn't dig a hole either. Learned his lesson about asking questions. Arm was all better now, mostly, but it got sore in the cold. Mrs. Aada said it was because D Jay broke it and it didn't heal proper.

The girl hugged her knees and looked around for something.

"You found my bike, huh?"

"Back there." Early pointed as he climbed down the ladder.

Sitting down by the girl he could see the white basket was still bent, the missing tassel still missing.

"Thought so. That crazy Mikki next door was screaming about someone trying to steal it. Said it was a big guy."

The girl wiped her purple lip with the back of her hand. Toby and Early got those when Mrs. Aada made a pitcher of that powdered Freshie, mostly sugar water and colour.

Freshie lips could last all day. Cherry was Early's favourite. Lemon lime was Toby's.

"Why are you staring?"

"Your hair."

"Cut it myself." Penny rubbed her head. "Used my project scissors. They weren't very sharp."

"What kind of project?"

"Oh, something stupid for my geography teacher, about Ceylon."

Early'd never heard of it.

"Country way over there." The girl pointed at the harbour. "I'm supposed to find pictures about factories and their dancing and clothes and stuff and stick 'em on bristol board. Got the letters coloured. I used a different colour for every letter and added sparkles."

Early said letters made with sparkles sounded pretty. Could he see?

"It's not done." The girl scooped up some rocks and started looking at each one with her right eye closed. "My mom didn't stop me from watching *The Forest Rangers*, so it's her fault. She's supposed to say no TV before homework. I got a detention. You ever think about being an Indian or a Mountie?"

Most times, Early didn't get past thinking about being with Toby.

"If I was a boy, I'd be just like Chub on *The Forest Rangers*, living in old forts with big dogs. Bet Chub doesn't care about stupid old islands beside India."

Early straightened up and stretched. "That why you cut your hair?"

"Huh?"

"To be like that fella, Chub."

"I guess so."

She told Early the locks were part of her and she couldn't just throw them away, not without a proper funeral. So she took an empty shoebox in her closet and with markers, she drew a cross on the lid, adding: Penny Ann Deforest RIP 1963. Each letter in a different colour, with sparkles. Then she marched slowly, one step at a time, and placed the coffin in the garbage.

Early thought she was sad about it now.

"No way. My mom making me wash and brush it all the time and saying don't get cooties, and Dad saying long hair's pretty on girls." She threw one of the rocks. "So now you have to call me Chub. Like Chub from *The Forest Rangers*."

"But that's a boy's name."

"I didn't ask to be born a stupid ol' girl. Girls don't get to be anything, 'cept secretaries, so now I'm Chub. No more dresses for me. And I only play with boys."

"Okay, Chub."

"So…where's that friend of yours?"

"Toby?"

"Yeah, him."

"He's not been good this week."

"What's the matter with him?"

"His grandpa says lots of things, weak here, weak there." Early rubbed his chest, then pounded his heart. "Nothin' the matter with his head though."

"He's a Negro. You know that?"

"Smarter than me, that's for sure."

"Mom sure wouldn't like being this close to 'em. Only Negro she saw was in that movie about Scarlett O'Hara, but I can't watch it because they say damn. They don't have 'em where she comes from. She wants to move back to Ottawa."

"Yeah?"

"They killed my baby brother, you know."

Maybe that was why Early didn't like foxes. One tried to get into the shed at night and almost sunk its teeth into Emily.

"No, this really happened. That house we live in? That was supposed to be Mom's dream house. They ruined it. Dad got it with money from the war."

"Toby's grandpa was in a war. He's got a wooden leg."

"My dad just has an extra heartbeat, so he wasn't really there. He worked in the office giving out pay. But Dad got money anyway for being good at that, and Mom wanted a house if she was going to move here and get married, but she didn't know about Negros being so close because Dad didn't tell."

She found out going off the road.

Chub said it was because that car her mom was learning to drive had too many buttons and gears. She was going to see how the house they were building was doing, only then, it was just a cement hole. She must've stepped on the wrong pedal and kept on going through alders and bushes, bounced all the way down over the train tracks. The woman whose yard she drove into ran and got folks to help when Chub's mom opened her eyes. Boy, did she holler.

"They were all black, Early."

"Maybe your mom was scared seeing folks come to help her."

"One of them slapped her in the face, and told her to stop screaming. Mom says her shakes started after they towed the car back up the hill and she lost the baby she didn't know she had. Would have been another big brother."

Chub said they included him in dinner grace.

"That's why she told those builders to turn the house around. Mom said she wasn't standing on our porch, looking every day at what killed my brother and made her sick. Bad enough she had to smell it, and that's why our hubcaps get stolen and she wasn't hanging laundry outside, 'cause that'd get stolen too."

Early wondered what D Jay would say about turning their trailer around, then rubbed his arm.

"So what if we don't use the living room except at Christmas? Mom makes Derek open the company's-coming table, but she closes the curtains. Means I get to see down here from my room. I like hearing those wind chimes."

Early made those for folks to keep away the birds coming to the dump and he'd make one for her.

"Now that you know me and Toby, you can tell your mom not to be scared."

Chub scratched at the dirt with her sandal.

"Can't tell my mom anything. Before she got really sick, Mom and Mrs. Venney used to get on the bus all the time and go down to the city hall and say it's not fair for people like Toby living there, making our house lose money. She'd be some mad if she caught me here."

Chub stood and pushed away hair that was no longer in her face.

"Whatcha doing up there on that trailer anyway?"

"Fixin' it so we don't get wet when it rains."

"Bet playing with Toby'd be more fun."

Good idea, so they started walking.

"Mrs. Venney next door says all this land is city property."

"Yeah?"

"She works for the city."

"Doin' what?"

Chub didn't know for sure, but there was lots of typing involved. Her bike was bobbing on the railroad ties as she pushed it between them.

"Don't you ever get scared living here?"

"What for?"

"My mom says Africville's no better than a dump, full of bad people."

"People don't live in the dump."

"Don't mean that, over there."

"No bad people there."

"What about all these shacks?"

"That place way up there with the Christmas wreath all dried out, that's Molasses Jack's, 'cause he comes from an island where they makes brown sugar. Taught here in the school for a long time. Gone now. Tried to teach me. Real nice too. That purple house behind him, that's Mr. Ganes. His missus saves shirts and pants from his boy Larry and gives 'em to me. Larry's goin' to the university. Mr. Ganes, he's a mailman. And see that tar paper? That's where Mrs. Battle lives."

"Looks kinda scary."

Chub squeezed her handlebars real tight.

"I could fix that basket."

"This old thing? My mother makes me take it everywhere. And it didn't get stolen. I threw it away."

Early couldn't get his head around that one.

"Where does Toby live?"

"Big Town." Early pointed to that part of Africville past the church where Toby said you made the longest shadows in summer. "See the green house? That's Mrs. Aada's. She's got a store. The one with the paint falling off? Toby lives there with his grandpa."

Chub wasn't looking at either house. She was staring at the shed between them.

"That? That's Aubrey's."

"There's a cow."

"Mrs. Trilby. She's Mrs. Aada's."

"I never saw a real one up close before."

"C'mon, she's friendly."

Early started to run. Chub hopped on her bike.

"Bet I can beat you."

"Bet you can't."

She tried, but Early went flat out. Got there just before her, both of them breathing hard in between giggles and

I-beat-you, no, I-beat-you. Chub sure was strong for a girl. Mrs. Trilby, a completely brown cow, was eating grass, not caring who won.

"Wanna pet her?"

"You can do that?"

"Sure."

They opened the gate, Early said to the cow this here is Chub, and they gave Mrs. Trilby a scratch between her eyes. Chub got a swat with the cow's tail for thanks.

"She likes you."

"What's that shed for?"

No time to answer because the old man was coming out the door of his house.

"Early, thought I saw you come by. Toby's inside. Who's this?"

Chub took a backwards breath.

"It's just Toby's grandpa."

"What's your name, young lady?"

Chub wasn't saying.

"It used to be Penny, now it's Chub. She doesn't want to be a girl anymore."

"I see. Miss Chub, pleasure to meet you. Everyone calls me Aubrey."

"Just plain ol' Chub. My mother says I have to call old people mister."

"Then it's Mr. Daye to you, but like I say, call me Aubrey. The other boys do. No point in having special rules just for you."

Something scratched at the door behind Aubrey.

"C'mon out, boy, and say hello."

Aubrey said that dog was 105 years old, only thing around older than him. He laughed when he said it. But then he said Ol' Nip sure was spry for a tubby old guy with thin wobbly legs, almost blind, and not hearing too well. Early could remember when Ol' Nip was black all over, but he had a lot of white around his mouth now. He gave Chub a short bark, more like half a bark, and a quick sniff. Aubrey said Ol' Nip liked her.

"Funny name for a dog."

"Used to eat turnips raw when he was a pup. Called him Turnip, course that got battered some, like things do. Couldn't eat enough of them. Still does, but I have to cook them soft now 'cause he's only got a couple of teeth left."

"Doesn't look like Spike. He's the dog on *The Forest Rangers*. He's huge."

Then Chub asked about the shed.

"Early not take you in there to have a look? Well, c'mon in."

Early and Aubrey, sometimes Toby if he was up to it, had been working on Jubilee Hall for almost five years. Even with sunflowers planted all around, it was a foolishly named eyesore as far as Mrs. Aada was concerned, and she said Aubrey built it just so she couldn't see into his kitchen.

The walls were made of bottles.

"Set them in the cement row on row right up to the roof. Lets the light inside. All different colours."

Aubrey sure did like showing the place off.

The door Early found in the dump had been hung. Aubrey found a bit of glass to fix the window Charlie

Savage broke. The building had a tin roof and on each corner Early attached a whirligig. He made those from forks and clothes hangers. Aubrey didn't want birds up there shitting on Miss Portia.

"Who's that?"

"Miss Portia White?"

Chub shook her head.

"Young lady, she's just the finest opera singer in the world. Used to teach singing here, when she was just a girl herself. I sat outside the school and listened to her. You've never heard a voice like hers. I know with a proper singing hall, she'll come back. And this place that Early helps me with is going to bring her to Africville to give a concert."

"Aubrey writes her a letter every week saying please come," Early said.

Inside wasn't finished yet, but Chub got to see the rainbow that Aubrey was talking about. Only happened at certain times on sunny days. Last summer, Early found a pile of wood, polished red, and enough for the floor. They still had to get something for folks to sit on when Miss Portia sang and of course, a stage.

Ol' Nip followed them inside and walked to the middle of the room, nails clip-clopping on the hardwood.

"It's the most beautiful place I ever seen, Mr. Daye."

Always pleased the old man to hear that. Aubrey closed up Jubilee Hall after they got outside and then had a look at the sunflowers coming up. Not much to see, just shoots of green.

"Better come inside the house and say hey to Toby."

The kitchen table took up most of the room. A sheet of green plastic covered the top, and there was always a bowl of oranges in the middle. Early loved oranges. Go ahead, help yourself, Aubrey said. An arch separated the kitchen from the other room, with windows open to see Tibby's Pond. Got lots of sun in there and Aubrey had the green thumb. He had plants growing right up to the ceiling that had to be cut back with scissors.

The walls had lots of pictures: Aubrey's folks gone to heaven, Mrs. Aubrey that he didn't talk about and she'd been dead a long time, Toby for sure, Toby's mom, Deborah, but she didn't live here, and Toby's old man, Knowl. Didn't see Knowl too much. He came and went now that he wasn't with Toby's mom anymore.

The hallway by the oil stove went back to the bedrooms, one for Aubrey, one for Toby. When Early slept over, Aubrey put down a mattress for him by Toby's bed. He covered it with a garbage bag in case Early peed in the night. Toby said he snored, but Early knew it was Ol' Nip doing it out in the hall. His pops'd beat the shit out of him if Early snored.

"Toby, son? You awake?"

Early almost didn't see him lying on a sofa shiny on the arms and backrest, covered over by Boston ferns, reading *The Whiteoaks of Jalna*. All his mom's Jalna books were on a shelf behind his bed, except the last one that told him how they all turned out. He couldn't get enough about rich folks in big houses.

"Early's come by with Miss Chub."

"Just Chub."

"Pardon me. Toby had a bad night with the asthma, didn't you, son?"

Toby, kind of pale, sat up, surprised to see the girl again.

"What happened to you?"

Early said she cut off her hair and old name, then explained about the bike.

"It wasn't stolen. I left it there on purpose. Wish it would get stolen."

"That pretty bike you left outside by the fence?"

"It's pink."

Mrs. Aada came through the back door. She was a big woman, but seemed even bigger in Aubrey's house. She had a plate of date squares.

"Who's this?" she said about Chub, not even bothering to say how'd you do.

"Friend of the boys here."

"Where you from?"

Chub pointed to the ceiling, but Early guessed she meant the hill they couldn't see because of the roof being in the way.

"Does your mother know you're here?"

"Sort of."

"Sort of sounds like a no, miss."

Chub told Mrs. Aada that her mom said she couldn't go past the iris curtain, that being a fence of blue flowers growing behind the house.

"How come you call it that?"

"It's like the iron curtain, you know, in Europe."

"Oh."

"Last year we had a real fence and we got rabbits burrowing underneath. Mom said I couldn't have one as a pet because she might trip over it and I'd better not feed them or we'd never get rid of them, but I did and one bit me. Mrs. Venney next door started yelling about rabies, so my dad poured gasoline down the holes and threw in a match. Rabbits came out like balls of fire. Guess that made the ground soft because next time it rained, crack opened up and took off part of the lawn. The part with the fence. Now I've got a pet snail. Wanna see?"

"Good Lord," said Mrs Aada.

"But I didn't go through the irises," said Chub. "I rode my bike by the prison fields and came down that way."

"That bit of fancy footwork wouldn't wash if you were my girl, but since you're not, get yourself around the table. You too, Toby Daye. I'll get some tea on if I can find where you've hid that pot on me, Aubrey."

Mrs. Aada made everyone help themselves to a date square, then bent with a groan, looking around for the teapot.

"Under the sink where I always keep it."

"Why you won't leave it over the stove? I can't keep bending down to get it and you've got mice down here."

"No one told you to make tea."

"Can't have date squares with no tea."

Toby slipped into the chair beside Chub and very quietly told her they weren't really fighting. When his ma, Deborah, and his father got into things, now that was something. People getting broken kind of fighting.

Mrs. Aada put the plates down and told them to have another square. Aubrey got water to boil.

"No thank you," said Chub, but she was staring down that date square.

Toby had his broken in two on the plate and was about to bite.

"Not hungry?"

"No, ma'am. I mean, yes, ma'am. My mother says I'm fat."

"Fat? Lord almighty, Aubrey, look at her. Skin and bones. Why does your mother think you're fat?"

"She says I am, that's all."

"Your mother a big lady?"

"Kinda. Being sick makes her that way."

"Your mom's poorly?"

Chub touched the side of her date square with her finger, then licked it. She said her mother had multiple cirrhosis.

"But my dad says she used to put on her wedding dress every anniversary and show off weighing five pounds less than the day she got married. She makes me ride my bike so I don't get fatter. But I'd rather take judo lessons with my brother, Derek. He has to this summer, but he doesn't want to. My dad's making him even though he's always yelling about how he's going to pay for beer on Friday nights and lights aren't assholes, they don't close by themselves. I guess 'cause stuff costs so much."

Mrs. Aada put her church face on and looked like she wanted to say something.

"Judo might be a good thing to learn," said Aubrey. "Could a man with one leg sign up?"

He stood and hopped around until Mrs. Aada tried not to laugh and told him to sit down again.

But Chub said her mom didn't think judo was for girls and because she was spending more time sick in bed, she couldn't be wondering what Chub was getting up to. So when summer came, Chub had to go to Brownie camp with her next-door neighbour.

"What do you do there?" Toby'd never heard of Brownie camp.

"Learn prayers and oaths and how to diaper babies and make stuff for a hope chest. But I'd rather do judo. Who wants to get married anyhow?"

"Good for you." Mrs. Aada slid another square onto Chub's plate. "I've been married twice, decent men mind you, but they don't live long enough so the only good thing I got left out of that is my boy Ralph. He's the deacon over at the church. And look at me. You think I'd want to get back into some old wedding dress fit for moths? Besides, you're too young to be thinking of such nonsense."

The kettle whistled.

"Now eat up," Mrs. Aada said.

"I never had tea before."

Toby asked Chub if she was poor.

"No, you are. I mean, people here are."

Mrs. Aada put the cups down before them. Mostly milk in Toby's and Chub's. Aubrey asked Early if he had ants in his pants and if he was so hungry he couldn't sit still then maybe he better eat another date square.

"Rich people can be poor," said Mrs. Aada.

Aubrey figured there'd be poor folks anywhere. Maybe up there, maybe down here.

"You don't have to look hard to see the poor folks here."

"Now, Aada, you know we're lucky, got these fine homes, good neighbours. Every morning I look out that window and see the boats in the harbour, and I say thank you, Jesus. You think we see that up in the city? We still got our church. We still got good times ahead."

Ol' Nip curled up in his bed by the oil stove with a long sigh.

"Trains in our backyards, no running water, no sewers, nothing other folks in this city got. I pay taxes. You pay taxes. And why is that boy of yours always sick?"

Chub was halfway to having another date square, but thought better of it and put her arms under the table.

"Boiling water before we drink it and that's if you can find any come summer. Why, is what I want to know. Lord help us, and you know this, Aubrey, when things get going on a Saturday night, boys get too much to drink, get fighting, sure, then the police come down to help Africville. Most times, we're on our own. Always on our own. Yes, I remember what it was like, before the city started circling around us like crows, before our school got torn down, and when you couldn't fit all the folks into the church come a Sunday. What've we got now? Nothing. Just a place for trash to come squatting, giving good folks a bad name."

Mrs. Aada meant D Jay, but Early knew she didn't mean any harm. Facts is facts, she liked to say.

"Things'll be different when Miss Portia comes to sing."

"Lord almighty, Aubrey. Every time I hear you go on about that woman I think you've lost your mind."

"All things being equal, she'll come."

"Old fool."

Aubrey smiled and nodded and held his ground. Toby told Chub not to worry; Mrs. Aada and Grandpa really are friends.

"I'll tell you this, Miss Portia knows where she comes from. She won't let us down."

"Miss Portia Miss Portia Miss Portia."

"And when she sings, everyone'll come. I expect even the mayor himself. He'll see how things are. We'll get water and sewers then. Maybe even a paved road."

"No city mayor is ever going to come here with buckets of money, Aubrey Daye."

"Could I come and hear Miss Portia sing?" asked Chub.

"I think we can keep a seat for you." Aubrey looked hard at Mrs. Aada. "I expect they'll fill up real quick though."

"Don't you be getting him started."

Too late. Aubrey was already pulling his scrapbook from under the sofa table.

"Look here, it's from a New York City paper, back during the war. Says of Miss Portia's concert, 'An Unheralded Star is Born.'" He pointed to each word with his finger, then he pulled out another clipping. "Look at this. She was commanded to sing for the Queen over in Charlottetown. Commanded. She had to do it because she was so good the Queen wanted to hear for herself."

"You think you're going to get Miss High-and-Mighty, singing for the Queen, here to sing in a shed made out of gin bottles?"

"Yes I do."

Mrs. Aada took her cup of tea with her to turn around and look out the kitchen window.

"How come she doesn't want that lady coming here?" Chub whispered to Toby. "And how come your grandpa is smiling?"

Toby didn't say. Early got himself another date square. Mrs. Trilby, out in the yard, was saying in her own way, someone get over here and milk me.

THE RACCOON GOT UNDER THE TRAILER WHEN
Early and D Jay were asleep. Made a mess. Early thought
it might be looking for a place to have its babies. D Jay
didn't give a shit. Had Early smoke it out. That didn't do
much for inside the trailer. When the raccoon came back a
few days later, scratching to get under, D Jay got out of bed
because no fucking way was he putting up with that shit
again. Grabbed a shovel and went outside with a flash-
light. Next thing Early heard sounded like a kid screaming.
When D Jay came back and climbed into bed beside him,
he was feeling all wet. Early thought his pops'd gone and
worked himself up a sweat. It wasn't until morning that he
saw all the blood.

Early found the poor critter by the car batteries he
pulled from the dump ready to take back to salvage. Its
head was squished, but its paws were trembling. D Jay told
Early he wouldn't be blubbering so hard if that raccoon ate
his chickens, then made him leave it there to scare off the
others.

Took three hours before those paws stopped twitching. D Jay wanted the carcass burned, and Early wasn't to cross him by burying it instead. D Jay didn't want its stink bringing the crows. Those were his orders before he left for Truro. D Jay got some work up there for a few days, what, he wouldn't say, and when he got home, better be no raccoons.

So Early made a ring of stones around the dead animal, covered it with wood, and got the fire going.

"Whatcha doing?" Chub hollered from the other side of the tracks.

"Gettin' a fire."

Good thing Chub didn't see the raccoon. Early figured she wouldn't be happy if she knew.

"Mom hates fires. Won't even let us have candles. Hey, I know. I could bring some marshmallows and we could toast them."

Chub ran her hand along a car bumper to see if it was dirty, then sat. The back wheel of her bike went around slowly where she left it on the ground.

"You're lucky."

He sure was, especially if marshmallows were coming his way.

"You get a whole summer doing nothing and your mother's not making you wear a Brownie uniform with puffy sleeves and stockings. I look like a hot dog."

"Toby says my mom's dead."

"Oh."

Early kicked at one of the burning logs with his foot.

"I'm practising how to karate-chop like Cathy Gale on *The Avengers*. Have you seen it? Wish I still had long hair. She can toss hers over her shoulder, like this."

"Your mom let you come down?"

"Dawn's babysitting me. She's Mikki's sister and tie-dyes her clothes. I like her, she's really neat and she doesn't care what I do. She even made a T-shirt for me, and she talks on the phone all day except when *Let's Make a Deal*'s on. She writes letters to a boy in Venice she met in a pen pal club. Got a funny name, Innocent, after a pope or something. He calls her Aurora 'cause that's what her name is in Italian. Can I put a log in the fire?"

Early handed her a piece of wood.

"You got lots of junk around here."

Mostly car parts and bales of wire, but they had some sinks and pots, a few toilets and furniture that needed mending. Early's neighbours were always saying having one dump is bad enough, Early, c'mon now, we don't need two. Maybe so, but he and Pops could get money for this.

"Hey, I remembered." Early ran to the chicken shed and brought back a can. "I got this from Mr. Welford's, where I fix cars. Gold paint for your bike."

Chub looked like she was trying to see the colour already on.

"Take off the basket and the tassel?"

"Sure."

"Thanks, Early."

Chub had a nice smile when you got a chance to see it.

"You leave that bike here and I'll do it."

"Oh, what'll I tell that snoopy Mikki?"

"Funny name for a girl."

"Her real name is ugly, Michaela. She thinks Brownies have to be best friends. She'll know my bike is gone. If she finds out it's down here she'll tell my mom."

Chub sure had big problems.

"I know! She won't follow me if I tell her I have to see my dad at his work before I go to camp."

"Yeah?"

Chub shrugged. "Been there before, on Gottingen Street. Makes books and stuff. Real noisy machines, but I like the ink smell. Dad says his boss is a damned Jew, but he's worked there for a long time, even before the navy took him, then he went back."

Early took Chub's bike and put it in the shed with the chickens. They'd keep an eye on it until he got back.

"Hey, got my allowance. Let's go to Mrs. Aada's and get something for Toby."

On the way, Mrs. Jensen was hanging laundry and waved hello. Early told Chub she used to work in Richmond. Still cleaned houses sometimes when her bones didn't ache.

Where the lupins poked through the bend in the train ties, Early walked balancing on one track, arms out, Chub on the other.

"Who's your new girlfriend, Early?"

Chub stuck a finger at Charlie Savage and told Early it meant up yours. They continued on, trying not to look at the laughing boy.

"What'll we get Toby?"

"He likes Cherry Blossoms."

"Then that's what we'll get. Hello, Mrs. Trilby. Miss me?"

The cow was eating grass behind Aubrey's Jubilee Hall, not missing a thing. Chub waited, like she expected Mrs. Trilby to say hello back.

Early liked being in Mrs. Aada's store, right there in her front room she could use since her boys moved on to heaven, except for the deacon. It was always warm inside, which was okay for winter, but Mrs. Aada liked it warm in summer too. And there was coffee waiting and cookies, usually with jam in the middle, just in case Blind Emmett made his way over for the company and the news according to Mrs. Aada. Mrs. Etta Briscoe was in there when Early and Chub showed up, saying something about hearing it herself and this time the city meant business.

"Hi, Mrs. Aada. I got money for Cherry Blossoms for me and Toby and Early."

"That's fine, honey, but you shouldn't be interrupting Mrs. Briscoe here."

"Aada, don't you talk to the girl like that."

"If her mother can't teach her a thing or two, then I will. Early, you know where the candy is."

Mrs. Briscoe was staring at Chub and Early like she was seeing something from the moon.

"I got papers," Mrs. Aada was saying back to her friend.

"It's not right. I've been here all my life. You too. Raised my kids here."

Early put three Cherry Blossoms on the counter and Chub handed over the cash.

"Strike it rich, honey?"

"Got my allowance."

"Good for you."

"You got marshmallows? Early's got a fire so we can toast them."

Mrs. Aada pointed to the shelf by the window.

"Early? That so? You're not messing with fire?"

"Just for my pops."

"Do I have enough money?"

"With some to spare, honey. You want a plaster for that cut on your arm?"

"Oh, it's okay."

"You saying hello then to Mrs. Trilby on your way over?"

"Already did."

They were out the door, running over to Aubrey's by a fence buried under a wave of black-eyed Susans.

"Hey? Whose car is that?"

Black with lots of chrome. Not new, but sure kept up with the polish.

Early knew that meant Toby's mom had come by. She had a place in town by the hotel next door to the train station. Whenever Toby's mom came by, his old man Knowl showed up too. Deborah, she was having a smoke at the table. Knowl, he was talking to her, real quiet, when Early and Chub came in. Aubrey was gone, maybe mailing a letter to Miss Portia. Might be a while if that's the case, he and Ol' Nip not walking so fast anymore.

"Early, who's this?"

"I'm a friend of Toby's. And Early's," said Chub.

"The little bastard is hiding in his room," Knowl said. "Hates seeing his old man."

"Maybe if you came around more often—"

"You only come by to lift a few bucks off your dad."

Early thought maybe he and Chub ought to get into Toby's room.

"Hey, Early, how come you won't work for me?"

"Pops wouldn't like it."

Knowl laughed. Big, wide laugh, but not the kind of laugh that made you feel good. He was a tall, thin man, as good to look at as Deborah was. He wore his hair shaved and had a part razored in. Always dressed in the best, that Knowl, smelled good too.

"Say, Early, where's your old man running?"

"Truro."

"He better see me before Saturday. You tell him I'm looking for him. Got it?"

Chub was tugging at Early. He thought she was wanting to eat those Cherry Blossoms. So would Toby, after he found out about them, but the boy said nothing, shoving a jug under his bed when they walked into his room.

"What stinks?"

"Nothing."

"Smells like bleach."

Toby turned his back towards them and pulled on a shirt over peeling skin.

"We got Cherry Blossoms and marshmallows. Wanna go to Early's? He's got a fire and we can toast them."

Toby didn't get a chance to say okay because of the screaming from the kitchen. Couldn't make out what Deborah was saying because of the furniture moving around.

"What's happening?"

Toby was already opening the bedroom window. They'd done this before.

"My folks fight a lot."

"That's okay, Toby. Your mom's right pretty for looking so sad."

Something glassy broke outside on Toby's door.

All three climbed out the window. Chub was laughing real hard. Toby got winded, so he climbed on Early's back. Good time for a Cherry Blossom. Toby unwrapped it and slid the whole thing into Early's mouth. Then he took one for himself, just a bite.

"Your folks get on, Chub?"

The snow started. Not the real thing, it being summer, but sometimes those flakes came down from the incinerator. Soft and white, taking their sweet ol' time to hit ground.

"Once, my dad had too much to drink and he slipped on the ice and got stitches over his eye." Chub had a mouthful of chocolate, so it came out kind of mumbly. "He came home with the policeman, who was his friend, after Dad hit him when he said bar's closed. Mom was real mad. Threw buns at him. My brother had to crawl under the kitchen table and get them. But mostly now, Mom doesn't talk so good."

When they got back to Early's trailer, the fire had burned so low that he had to put on more logs. Chub snapped off some alder branches for toasting the marshmallows.

Toby watched her and smiled.

AUBREY TOLD EARLY YOU STAY CLEAR OF
Isleville Street to get to work. Early knew every dog by
name, and if he saw one playing on the grass-covered
boulevards under the elms of those townhouses the city
built for folks after the big explosion, Aubrey said he'd
catch shit for sure for being late. Maybe that's why Mr.
Welford said you can't come in Early. Go home like I told
you before.

Early sat on the sidewalk out front underneath the roof.
Didn't Mr. Welford want Early to drain those oil pans?
Then Ben came and sat alongside him. Why are you sitting
here in the rain, Early? You know Mr. Welford said you
can't work here anymore.

But there were cars to fix.

Early had to have it explained again: You can't be
stealing paint from Mr. Welford. That was why he couldn't
come to work anymore.

Early remembered. D Jay wouldn't be happy when he
found out. Ben didn't like D Jay. Whenever D Jay showed

up at Mr. Welford's to collect Early's pay, Ben looked like he wanted to do something with a fist.

So Early headed back, but it didn't feel right doing that in the middle of the day when Ben had all those cars to fix by himself. By one of the red and white electrical towers sitting on top of Africville, Early found a good sitting place, where Barrington Street got back to just dirt. Nice view of what Aubrey called the Narrows, and over there, the pier where D Jay got work sometimes. Real nice patch of blueberries there, but they were nowhere ready for eating.

There was only one thing to do. That made Early smile.

Toby was in, reading one of his thick books.

"You're supposed to be at work," Toby said, opening his window because Early had tapped on it.

"Ben says I can't go there anymore."

"How come?"

"I took paint."

"Early, you stealing from Mr. Welford?"

"Stealin's wrong."

"What about the paint?"

"Chub needs it for her bike. She can't ride her pink one."

"Your pa'll be mad."

"Yeah?"

"Better get in here."

Aubrey poked his head in Toby's room and told Early he was too big to be crawling in through windows. Go around to the front door, young man. So Early did.

Early had made six marks on the back of the chicken shed so it must be Saturday night and he all but forgot about Mr. Welford. Too bad getting to where Early could scratch that seventh mark took longer than all the others together.

When D Jay came home he told Early to get those jugs he brought out of the truck.

"And don't drop them because you know that fucking jungle bunny charges me four bucks apiece for that cat piss of his."

D Jay always laid in a supply of shine from Toby's dad for his Saturday night card games. When the men came over, Early had to sleep in the shed with the chickens. He didn't mind. It was no fun being around those men when they got to drinking. Got real smoky in that trailer too. Early'd rather sit in the shed talking to the girls, that's what he called his chickens, thinking about meeting up with Toby in the morning, and those big pancakes Mrs. Aada made.

D Jay handed Early his razor and a bar of soap.

"Get down to the water and scrub. Make sure you don't cut yourself."

Washing up in the harbour wasn't so bad, but Early didn't care for shaving with cold water. When he got back to the trailer, D Jay was looking over the clothes hanging on the back of the door.

"You got a good shirt?"

D Jay pulled Early's other shirt off the hook and took a smell. Then he got one of his, a checkered one, and tossed it at Early.

"Put this on. You know I want you clean for Saturday nights."

When the first truck pulled in front of the trailer, Early didn't have to be told to go wait in the shed.

The card playing and drinking could get real loud, even break into fighting. The neighbours hated that, and told Early we'd get the cops on your daddy, but you're lucky they won't come down here on a Saturday night. The card playing didn't sound like it was getting out of hand this night. Maybe nobody'd come. Early thought about what he and Toby'd do in the morning. Maybe go out on their raft. Maybe help Aubrey with Jubilee Hall. Eat eggs and sausage for sure.

With the rain and the wind, Early barely heard anything until that knock, shy like a child did it, or maybe Toby.

But it wasn't Toby.

Early couldn't see the man's face too well. He rarely saw the faces of the men D Jay sent over. Didn't want to anyhow. Smelled them though. Saw the crests on their arms when they held him down. This one smelled of cigarettes and onions, like maybe his wife had made meatloaf that night for dinner. Tonight it was Mr. Navy again. Early didn't know what the man's real name was. Mr. Navy was nice enough, short, shaved his head, and had a blue ship with a crest tattooed on his forearm. Early saw him once down on Barrington Street heading into the base. He was wearing a uniform with shiny buttons and a gold dolphin on top of his stripes. Early hollered and waved, but Mr. Navy pretended he didn't know him. Early sure got the what for from D Jay later when his father found out about Early trying to say hello.

"I'm losing big time tonight, buddy." Mr. Navy had water on his face from the rain. "So make it quick, okay? Gotta get back."

Mr. Navy liked Early to pull his dick from his pants and work it with his hand and spit until it got hard.

"That's right."

He held the back of Early's head and made him swallow. Sometimes Early got big ones and choked, but Mr. Navy fit nicely and didn't push too hard.

"I wish my ol' lady'd suck dick like you, kid."

He kept Early working with his mouth and hands like he was milking Mrs. Trilby until Mr. Navy started to make noise and didn't let go before he let loose. Then he got all fidgety zipping up and smiled at the chickens so he didn't have to look at Early.

"You still working over at Welford's?"

Early wiped his mouth.

"No, sir. Took some paint."

"Too bad. See ya, kid."

That left Early alone with his girls. They were quiet and Early thought they looked sad. Emily was poorly, not eating well. She wasn't as big as the other chickens. Early just had to remember to ask Aubrey what to do.

The shed door opened. D Jay was there, wet like Mr. Navy was.

"You fuckin' bastard. You lose your job?"

D Jay never waited to get answers. He used his boot. Early knew it'd go quicker if he curled up on the ground. The chickens were squawking and flapping all over, trying not to get hit, feathers everywhere. Things didn't die down until Early gave up trying to shield himself.

"Get up."

His old man's breathing was hard as he pulled Early into the rain. It was late. Only light was that one coming on the tracks. When Early got dragged past the trailer, one of the men inside yelled what's up with the kid? Early'd never seen him before, so he must've been new, or he wouldn't have asked.

When they got on the tracks, Early tried to pull away.

"I said, kneel, goddamn ya."

"Hey, D Jay—" The new fella didn't finish.

"Shoulda done this when you were born."

"D Jay, c'mon on, lay off the kid."

That light was coming right at him.

"You know what I had to go through to get you that job?"

"I'm sorry, Pops."

"I'm done with you, you fucking little cocksucker."

That's when Mr. Navy said, "Let him go."

D Jay pulled tight around Early's neck. Early didn't make any noise after that. The train did, letting out a blast.

"You telling me how to deal with my kid?"

"For Christ's sake man, let him go."

Early felt the tracks vibrating and pulled hard against his father's hand.

"Fuck."

"Let him go!"

Just before the train click-click click-clicked by, Early's father yanked him out of the way. Then he laughed.

"C'mon fellas, you didn't think I was gonna do it?"

Someone at the trailer wanted to know if they were going to get back to playing cards or not. D Jay said he could use a drink.

Left there in the rain felt good to Early, especially on the parts that were bleeding.

Loud whispering woke Early to a dry soft bed and smells like something burning.

"Grandpa and Mrs. Aada fixed him up last night."

"Dog get at him?"

"No, his dad."

"Poor Early."

Early knew those voices, so he was happy to let them talk.

"How'd you get down here today?"

"My dad's working."

"On Sunday?"

"I know, eh? Mom says he never worked on Sundays

before, and Dad says they got a big order that has to go out and I have to help."

"That okay?"

"Yeah, only we don't go to his work. He takes me to the diner across the street and buys me a Coke. I like it with ice cubes. That's when some lady he works with comes in. She's got bubbles all over her face and she smiles a lot when she talks to Dad. Then when I'm finished my Coke my dad says to go back home because I'll just get in the way, and don't tell Mom. Gives me a dollar."

Toby and Chub were sitting on Toby's bed next to Early's mattress on the floor. The window was open. Outside, Mrs. Aada was yelling at Charlie Savage to stay away from those cardboard boxes she was burning in an oil drum, back of her store. Burning was the only way to keep the cockroaches from getting back into her house.

"You okay, Early?"

"You don't look so good." Chub put her hand on his forehead.

"What are you doing that for?"

"My mom used to do it when I was sick."

Aubrey said hello.

"How we doing?"

"We're gonna go swimming," said Chub.

"Maybe not today."

"But I'm okay now. We can go." Early brightened right up.

"First thing," said Aubrey, "we're all going over to Mrs. Aada's. She's got breakfast waiting. Then you can swim. Salt water'll be good for those cuts you got, Early."

Getting over to Mrs. Aada's was slow on account of Ol' Nip and Early not walking so fast, and Chub having to pet Mrs. Trilby.

"Aubrey Daye, look at this boy." Mrs. Aada slid pancakes onto Early's plate. "One day that D Jay Okander is going to—"

"Now, missus."

"Well, he'll go too far."

"Let's just have breakfast, let the boys head out for a swim."

Chub grinned at being one of the boys.

"Early, what's this I hear about losing your job? That so?"

"Yes, ma'am."

"That why your father did this?"

He nodded.

"It's not right what he did, but Early, you're almost a grown man. You got to keep working."

"Leave him be for the summer, Aada."

"Yes, fine, sun may be free from the good Lord, but food isn't. How's the boy to keep himself with that father of his?"

Chub and Toby were making faces and whispering.

"You two got something to say, we've all got ears."

"I was just asking Toby why Early lost his job."

"I expect that's between him and Mr. Welford. That right, son?"

"Ben says I took stuff."

"Early Okander, is that so?"

"Yeah, I guess."

When Mrs. Aada got her mind wanting to know something, Aubrey said it sure could spoil an appetite.

"You guess? That's your trouble, boy, you can't think past the end of your nose. Going to get you into trouble."

"Yes, ma'am."

Aubrey started asking who wants more syrup, and Toby and Chub said, I do I do.

"Now who's that poking around out there?"

Nothing got past Mrs. Aada, even while serving pancakes. Certainly not the two men passing her kitchen window, white shirts and ties, jackets slung over their shoulders. Aubrey had a look for himself and thought the men looked official.

"Maybe they're here for the baptizing over at the church. You know we got that reverend visiting from Preston."

"Could be from the city," said Chub. "Mrs. Venney told my mom they're going to do something about making people in Africville go."

"Go where?"

Chub didn't get that far with her overhearing.

"Now Aada, take it easy. How often have we heard that?"

"Yes, well, I've been hearing things too."

Aubrey was smiling. "Real good pancakes this morning, Aada. Real good."

Mrs. Aada wanted to know from Chub where her mother and this Mrs. Venney person thought they'd all go.

"She says you can go to hell for all she cares."

After Chub got a mind-your-mouth-miss, Mrs. Aada told Toby to stop feeding the dog.

Chub didn't think that was fair, her just repeating what her mother said.

"The city can come around and look all they want. It's a free country."

"There, Aada, why get worked up?"

Chub was looking at Mrs. Aada's grey crinkly hair and wanted to know from Toby if it was hard. He said no, touch mine, see?

"I suppose then, you've got deeds in order for that shack of yours, Aubrey Daye? Huh? Do you?"

"Sure, somewhere. And that's no shack, just needs some fixing. You know my daddy left it for me clear when he passed on. Besides, I'm not worried."

"And why's that?"

Aubrey put his fork down.

"Like I told you, Miss Portia's going to come and sing."

"Oh, you stupid old fool."

Breakfast out of the way, Mrs. Aada asked Toby to milk Mrs. Trilby, and Aubrey thought it would be nice for Chub and Early to stack cans in the store as a way of saying thanks to the old woman for cooking. But Mrs. Aada came up to Early quiet-like and said sit down and rest, you.

Chub didn't mind stacking for two and when they were done, Toby too, they ran over to Tibby's Pond, some faster than others.

Chub took off her shirt and shorts. She had a bathing suit on underneath, with straps around her neck and a frilly skirt around her belly. She hated it. Toby and Early got down to their underwear. Toby jumped in and told Early to hurry up, the salt in the water would only make his cuts sting for a minute.

First there was a lot of splashing.

"No, no. You have to really swim, like this."

Chub threw her arms back and forth, kicking her legs at the same time.

"Don't you guys know how?"

Nope.

"I take lessons after Brownie camp. I'll teach you."

Toby thought that would be okay.

"Lie back in the water. I got you, you won't sink. Now start kicking your legs."

That's when Toby's T-shirt floated up, showing those patches all over his stomach.

"Your skin's falling off."

Toby stopped kicking his feet and giggling and quietly waded to the beach. Chub followed.

"Where you going?"

Early stayed in the water, lying on his stomach with his head up so he could walk along the sandy bottom with his hands.

"How come you got those sores?"

Toby wasn't saying.

"He gets them because of that water he puts on himself."

"Shut up, Early."

"You mean that stuff you had in your room, smells like bleach? Mom uses that for cleaning."

"I'm not dirty."

"Just not the same as us, Chub."

"Hey look, over there. They're baptizing folks."

The clapping and singing procession from the church to the waterfront got them all back into their clothes, carrying on because it looked like they wet their pants. Toby was having an okay breathing day, which was good because Early had too many bruises to carry him.

Deacon English and that visiting preacher from Preston were dunking two men and a lady into the harbour. Early said like cookies in tea. Those being baptized were covered head to toe in white robes and everyone watching carried on with the singing and clapping and swaying.

"How come they do that?" asked Chub.

"It's for washing out sins."

"That so?" Early didn't know that, or if he had, he forgot.

"I'm Catholic," said Chub. "Got that washing done when I was a baby. This looks way more fun."

Toby said you had to be twelve.

Deacon English waved them over when he looked to be done with the dunking.

"What happened to you? Your dad at you again?"

Early didn't say.

Deacon English looked over in the direction of D Jay's trailer.

"One of these days I'm going to have a chat with that man." Then he noticed the girl. "Who's this?"

"Chub," said Toby.

"So you're Toby's girlfriend. My mother told me about you."

"I'm nobody's girlfriend."

The deacon apologized, but he was laughing too.

"Chub wants to get baptized."

"You do?"

"I hate my church. Makes me want to throw up when they use incense and they don't sing the good songs you do."

"You're young for baptizing. Have you been to one of our services at the church here?"

Chub shook her head.

"Then you'll have to come. Bring your folks."

Those people who'd got their sins washed away were finished swimming. Early said it must have worked. They looked like they were shining from way down inside. Deacon English asked the kids if they were coming to the church for the rest of the service.

"Can't. Early's got a surprise for Chub."

"Yeah, I got a surprise." He'd been holding on to it all week.

He wanted to tell Chub right there, but Toby said to wait until they walked along the train tracks to the trailer. D Jay wasn't back yet, so Chub and Toby followed Early behind the chicken shed where he showed them the bike.

"That's a real nice job," Toby said.

"Gold's my favourite colour. Thanks, Early. You want first ride?"

Early thought Toby would like a go even more, but Early didn't say. Toby'd hate Chub knowing that he never learned how.

SOMEONE THREW OUT A STAIRCASE WITH RAIL-
ings and posts of mahogany, so shiny Chub said it didn't
look like anyone had ever been up or down it, except
maybe a rich lady with slippers.

Chub had a clothespin on her nose. It left a red mark
and she talked funny, but she said it worked against the
stink.

"You think rats can bite through my rubber boots?"

Toby said they were more scared of her than she was of
them. He was sitting in his wagon by the road. When Chub
and Early brought him stuff out of the dump, he put it into
a pile. One for Aubrey because Jubilee Hall needed a stage.
The other for Early to sell for D Jay at the salvage yards.
Toby coughed while he waited for them to find stuff, but
Early could tell he was happy Chub came down to help.

"It's easy now," she said. "No one cares what I do, not
since Derek got walking pneumonia."

Toby wanted to know if you could die from it.

"Oh yeah, but I don't think my brother will."

"How you catch it?"

"The doctor said from Derek hanging out his bedroom window all winter in his underwear talking to Eddie next door."

"You gotta stay in bed?"

"Derek doesn't. He just wears his pyjamas in the house all day. So Eddie's sister doesn't have to babysit me and my brother thinks I'm being quiet in my room."

Early tugged at something under a bunch of wet boxes smelling of oil.

"What you got there?" Toby walked over with Chub to get a better look.

Chairs from a movie theatre, four stuck together. The stuffing was coming out of the seats because the rats had gotten in there first, but Early was sure Aubrey would be happy to see them.

"You're right, Early. And Mrs. Aada could get covers on them. Look brand new, then."

Getting the chairs out of the dump took the three of them. Chub and Early carried, and Toby told them where to watch their steps. When Early got them on the wagon and pulled it back to Aubrey's, Chub and Toby kept their hands on the chairs so the wagon wouldn't tip.

Aubrey saw the chairs coming from down the road. Started to two-step and almost fell off his wooden leg. Said it served him right to be jitterbugging past his prime.

"Don't you be leaving that garbage in the yard," Mrs. Aada said, watching from her window. "And don't you leave it near Mrs. Trilby or she'll eat the stuffing."

"You find this for me, Early?"

He wanted to say yes, but instead asked who that girl was on the blue bike, up the road, watching them.

"Oh no," said Chub. "It's that stupid kid next door."

"Penny, I thought we were going to make cupcakes for Brownies?"

Chub said she'd rather be behind bars in Rockhead, because no way was she baking cupcakes unless she filled them with pepper.

"I told you not to follow me and go home."

She yelled the last bit.

"I know where you go, Penny. I'm telling your mother."

"My name's not Penny."

Ol' Nip gave a bark.

"That your friend, Chub?" Aubrey waived Mikki to come closer.

"No way."

"You can't leave her over there."

Chub stomped over to sit by her bike with Toby on the steps of Jubilee Hall.

"She wouldn't leave me alone after camp. I told her not to follow me." She kicked the wheel and sent it slowly spinning.

"Where's your bike, Penny?"

"It *is* mine, stupid."

Mikki was circling closer, but she wasn't getting off her bike. When she stopped, she was shaking.

"Penny, can we go home? I'm afraid being here. I think I saw a mouse."

"Probably a rat, and I told you a million times, my name is Chub. And you go. Didn't ask you to follow me."

Aubrey said Mikki was afraid only because she didn't know everyone, so that was Toby, there's Early, he was Aubrey, the little fellow at his feet was Ol' Nip, and the cow out back, that was Mrs. Trilby.

"Penny, I have to pee."

Someone was going to have to show her the outhouse. Toby nudged Chub.

"Oh, all right."

Mikki got off her bike and ran over, stopping where Ol' Nip wanted to have a sniff.

"He won't hurt you. C'mon."

Chub had to take Mikki's hand and lead her around the back. They came back really fast because Mikki said there were too many flies.

"Wanna see the cow?" asked Toby, by way of a hello.

"Let's go home, Penny."

"If you do," said Aubrey, "you'll be missing Mrs. Aada bringing us something to drink. Why don't you have a rest, then Chub can ride home with you?"

"Let's go now. It's all garbagey 'round here."

Mikki was looking at Jubilee Hall with the sunflowers bobbing alongside the walls when she said that.

"That's where Portia White's gonna come and sing."

"Early, she doesn't know who that is."

Toby whispered go show her the rainbow.

"Oh, yeah," said Chub, "come and see. You'll like this."

The light was reflecting through the bottles when they went inside, except Mikki. She peered in from the door.

"What smells?"

"That's from the wood the boys brought back this morning. It's just a bit wet. After it's dry, won't smell a thing."

"Yeah, Chub," Early said. "Come see. I got buildin' the stage—"

Mrs. Aada showed up, pushed Mikki out of her way, and must have forgot about bringing something for everyone to drink.

"Early Okander, what did I tell you about messing with fires? You get yourself back to your place. I can see from my kitchen window, there's smoke coming from that way."

That set Ol' Nip barking more than he'd done in a long time as everyone ran outside to have a look.

"Will the firemen come?"

Mrs. Aada gave one of those unfunny laughs of hers.

"Best you can do around here if there's a fire is get out as much as you can. Early, where's your pa?"

"Dunno."

"Penny, can we go now?"

"You go. I have to help."

"None of you kids are going near that fire," said Mrs. Aada. "Early, get over there yourself."

Chub was on her bike.

"C'mon," she said to Toby. "Get on my seat. I can ride us both."

Chub and Toby and Mikki dropped their bikes back of the road and came along just as the flames took over the trailer, punching through the roof and out the windows. The chickens were okay though.

Mikki wanted to know why the fire trucks weren't there.

"There's no water," said Toby.

"Lots there." The girl meant the harbour.

Early remembered those nice sprinklers Chub had watering her lawn.

"D Jay'll be mad. Where do I sleep now?"

"You stay with me and Grandpa."

The chickens?

"Come back and feed them. Maybe Grandpa'll find someplace for 'em."

"Mrs. Trilby won't like chickens visiting."

"Aw, she won't mind."

"Uh oh."

A pickup truck bounced over the tracks crossing the dirt road, spraying the kids with gravel as it slid to a stop.

"Goddamn it to hell!" D Jay was out of his truck, running around the fire like he couldn't believe it was really burning. "Shit! Shit! Shit!"

D Jay grabbed Early by his shirt.

"You have any idea what kinda trouble I'm in?"

Then he was kicking the ground and anything else he could reach. Early stood back with the other kids just in case D Jay wanted to have a go at them. When D Jay looked like he might just do that, Chub took Toby's hand.

"Better go."

"Yeah."

"We gotta get our bikes," said Mikki, already running. "Hope they're not stolen."

She pedalled fast and didn't look back, bobbing up and down, her bum never once touching the seat.

But D Jay didn't hit Early. He spun around, kicked high, and put a dent in the side of his truck. Then he turned and pointed a shaking finger at his boy, but it was like something had a hold of his throat and he couldn't get words out.

They stopped on the tracks to catch their breath when they could see that D Jay wasn't coming after them.

"You see that? He was mad, Early."

But Chub was wrong. Early knew his pops and if anything, D Jay looked scared.

MRS. AADA BLAMED THE FIRE FOR TOBY STARTING to wheeze again and told Aubrey so at breakfast while she measured out coffee.

"All we need is a good northeast wind to clear away all this heavy August air," Aubrey said. "He'll breathe just fine."

"With all the bad wells around and boiling orders, don't you think it might be the water making Toby sick?"

"First it's smoke, now it's water. What is it, missus?"

"When are you getting that boy to a doctor, is what I want to know."

Early was reaching for another of Mrs. Aada's breakfast rolls. "You need a doctor, Toby?"

"No he doesn't, because I'm not letting some doctor cut parts off my grandson."

"Aubrey, fine thing to say in front of the boys."

"And drinking bad water is what gets you used to the germs."

Mrs. Aada set the coffee pot on the table and looked like she had more to say, but a truck stopped in front of the house. She peeked through the curtains over the sink.

"Early, it's your father."

Mrs. Aada put the latch on the screen door before D Jay could open it.

"He in here?"

"He's having breakfast."

D Jay pounded the door frame. "Burn my place down, even the tires melted, and you sit in there eating?"

Aubrey said the fire wasn't Early's fault.

"Then whose is it, old man? Early, you get out there and start putting up a new place. You hear me?"

"But how, Pops?"

"Shut up. And make it big, Early. You owe me that, you stupid shithead. Don't make me come after you."

Ol' Nip growled.

"How can you speak to your own boy like that?"

Aubrey said Mrs. Aada should leave it be and sit down at the table.

"You don't want to be in my business, old woman."

"I know your business, D Jay Okander. Everyone knows your business. Bringing men down here to drink and gamble and God knows what. You're trash."

"Aada—"

"And what you did to that poor boy's mother."

D Jay pressed his face against the screen.

"Shut your fuckin' mouth you meddling old cunt, 'cause you sure don't want your place to go up in flames too."

After D Jay drove off, Aubrey sat missus down at the table and poured her a cup of coffee. She pulled a tissue from her apron pocket and wiped her eyes.

First time Early ever saw tears on Mrs. Aada.

✳

Early started building while the trailer was still smoking and his eyes watered from the melted tires on the roof. First thing he built was a lean-to in the trees at the bottom of the hill for Toby to sit under, out of the sun so he could bring one of his Jalna books and he'd tell Early what those Whiteoaks were up to. When he got to a real funny part, he'd go hey, Early, come and hear this. Toby sure didn't have any trouble with letters flying across the page like Early did. Maybe Mrs. Aada didn't mean it when she said Toby was going to be stupid because he was sick from school so much.

As Toby read, Early cut and hammered. No plans, he just walked around the new place in his head, like being inside of a car that needed fixing. That reminded him of Mr. Welford's garage and his friend Ben.

"Miss me?" asked Chub.

They did, and that's why Early and Toby were happy and surprised when she came down through the trees, gave a knock on the back of the lean-to, and scared Toby into thinking it was D Jay.

"Thought you were in trouble," Toby finally got out between breaths going in.

"Me too. Mikki kept her trap shut 'cause I showed her how to do double Dutch. Hey, Early, whatcha building?"

"New place for Pops."

"Almost forgot." Chub handed over a peanut butter jar filled with water-looking something to Toby. "I got you some bleach. Here, smell it."

She opened it for him.

"I put some bath stuff in it so it smells nice. Want some on?"

"Maybe later."

Chub crawled under the lean-to alongside him. Early worked in the sun.

"Where've you been?"

"Aw, nowhere. My Aunt Joy's here. She's not really my aunt. She's just my mom's best friend. Didn't even know she was coming. She called from the train station and wanted someone to get her, so me and Derek had to go with my dad."

"She like visitin' you?"

Chub shrugged. "I think she wants to go back home. She says the buildings on Barrington Street remind her of some old place where she and Mom went skating when they were girls. A barn with a rink in it that smelled of cow turds and grease and the roof fell in when the snow got heavy. Aunt Joy said it was really hot in there in the summer and starlings nested in the rafters, but in the winter you froze and maybe even got piles sitting on the cold benches. But I guess the canteen made good hot chocolate because that's where my Uncle Ernie got her one on their first date. Now she doesn't even have a suitcase and she couldn't bring me and Derek presents 'cause she ran away with twelve dollars in her pocket."

"Who'd she run away from?"

Chub wasn't sure, but after some phone call her Aunt Joy got from a woman telling her in the middle of making dinner for eight people that she's her husband's girlfriend and her two-year-old boy is his, and then spending all that time on a train from Ottawa, she asked Chub's dad to stop the car by Rockhead Prison. Aunt Joy said the sea air might make her feel better, so she rolled down the window.

"That help?"

"She said no matter how bad things get, there's always those worse off. She meant some guys kicking a ball around under the power lines here 'cause my dad said you guys made houses from the dump."

Chub said her aunt was going to live in the room her dad built in the basement from wood and panels that was supposed to look like old wood and you had to duck your head under the furnace pipe by the washing machine to get in. Derek was supposed to move down there, but Chub said he didn't want to live in the cellar.

Early thought the room sounded neat.

"No it's not. It doesn't even have a door. My Uncle Ernie makes Coca-Cola so Aunt Joy's used to a big house. Bigger than ours."

"How long is your aunt staying?" Toby wanted to know.

Chub couldn't say, and although she liked her aunt and having her around meant she had less chores to do for her mother, she did think it was going to be hard sneaking out of the house.

"She's taking my brother to the doctor today to get a needle in his bum."

Toby asked how he was doing, walking around with pneumonia.

"Well enough to get into a big fight last night. Dad said it was time for Derek to get his hair cut and Derek said no way because he's growing it like the Beatles. My dad said no son of his is going to look like a Limey ta-ta and dragged him down into the basement and told Derek he'd better shut up or he'd cut it all off. My brother can be such a big baby. He said no no no what will Eddie say and my dad goes, right, it's coming off. Shaved him. Says he looks like a puker now, that's what they call boys in the navy. Dad said it would do Derek good to be in the navy, make a man out of him, but Derek's just worried what Eddie'll think about his hair."

Early wondered if Chub's brother would want a tattoo on his arm.

"Hey, Toby, how come you're sitting under here? Not feeling well?"

"My grandpa says to not get excited on hot days."

"How about a swim?"

"Better not."

"If you could do anything, what?"

"Sure wish I could play baseball instead of just watching Early."

"You guys play baseball?"

"Grandpa used to be on the Rangers, over there, across from Kildare's Field. He was the manager or something. Even had jerseys."

"Any girls on the team?"

"Girls can't play."

Chub wasn't happy about not playing ball or being a girl. Maybe both. Toby put the smile back on her face when he showed her his book.

EARLY WIPED THE SWEAT OUT OF HIS EYES AND started to take off his pants. He'd already taken his shirt off, being hot out there in the sun, but Toby said he'd better leave the pants on.

"C'mon out of the sun for a while."

Early looked towards the tracks and where the dirt lane passed over. D Jay wouldn't like it if he wasn't working.

"Ah, it's okay. We can see if he's coming."

Sure was nice lying beside Toby in the lean-to. Cool, wet air from the harbour felt good when you'd worked up a sweat, thinking about going for a swim, but looking at the shiny water made you squint. Early told Toby he was pretending to float away, right out into the basin, maybe end up on a ship and say howdy-do to the captain who'd say no more building, Early, because we got to sail to China. Up that high, he said he could look down on all the houses and fences leaning this way and that, and that the reds and yellows and blues coming up and grass growing over the roads didn't make you see so much yards full of rusting car pieces, and wood rot and shitters smelling ripe.

"Maybe it's too hot for Chub to visit."

"Yeah, Toby."

Some kids were hoop-de-dooping on the train tracks, but Early couldn't see them.

"Picking blueberries soon for Mrs. Aada, huh?"

"Soon."

"Maybe Mrs. Aada'll make Freshie and come by, huh?"

Toby was looking at the pieces of wood standing up where Early had put them for D Jay's new place.

"She doesn't like coming 'round, Early. Makes her sad thinking about the old days, when your dad didn't live here. Grandpa had a good job and lots of people asked Mrs. Aada to clean their houses. Now we just pick through garbage, waiting for Miss Portia."

Made no sense to Early about good stuff being behind him, or somewhere 'round the turn. Why not just be happy in the middle?

"That tree in Deacon English's yard'll be all butterflies soon, Early. Chub'll miss seeing it. Maybe we better go tell her."

After Toby put the idea into Early's head, the rest came easy.

"She gonna see us?"

"Sure, but we gotta watch for that dog you said is next door."

Up the hill they went, Toby on Early's back, through where the dogwood got thick, crossing over the old cotton mill tracks. Toby said they had to crawl through the blue irises growing under the sumac trees behind Chub's place so they didn't get caught, but Early had to stop and catch water getting tossed around in a big circle from the sprinkler.

"You hear that?"

Sounded like a rope creaking.

When Early saw the body hanging from the tree, he stood up, but Toby grabbed his arm and yanked him down.

"Hey!"

Chub jumped off the big knot at the end of the tree rope she'd been swinging on.

"Be quiet. My aunt'll hear you. She's downstairs in the kitchen with my mom."

"Where've you been?"

"Sick."

"What's the matter?"

"Got the runs. Doctor says what I got usually comes from bad water. I can't go far from the toilet."

"You gonna be sick long?"

"I dunno, do I? Hope I get better soon though. Mikki comes over every day and wants to play with Barbies. How's Mrs. Aada and Mr. Aubrey and Ol' Nip? They miss me?"

"Yeah, they're good."

"I miss them. Do anything to get away from here. Hey, Early, I can hear your bird chasers at night when it's windy."

Sure sounded like good ol' Chub even if she was whiter than usual.

"Can you come over soon?"

"I hope so. Has Miss Portia come yet?"

Toby said, "Naw."

"Good. Don't want to miss the concert."

Somebody inside the house asked Chub who she was talking to.

"You better go."

She ran to the porch and gave a quick wave before she went in the house.

They stayed hidden in the irises until the neighbour's door opened and out came that yappy dog. Saw them or smelled them, Early didn't know which, but he hit the grass barking.

Toby grabbed Early's arm, but the dog was tied to the clothesline and went flying backwards. Even so, no point staying put in case someone came out to see what was going on, so Early swung Toby on his back.

"I'm glad we saw Chub," Toby said, holding branches out of Early's face as he got over the train tracks.

Early was glad too.

D Jay was waiting by the shed when he came out of the trees with Toby, wanting to know where the fuck the lazy bastard had been.

Toby's dad was with him. Didn't look happy. Neither of them.

"You're supposed to be working on this, and all I find are these goddamned chickens crapping all over the place."

Early said he had to let them out of the shed to stretch their legs and get some fresh air.

Knowl was walking around, in and out, of D Jay's new place. Not hard to do with no walls yet.

"This ain't going to be ready for Saturday," he said.

Toby started to wheeze.

"Get on home, boy. You got no business being here."

Toby slid off Early's back, but didn't go anywhere.

"Look, I said I'd have a place ready and I will. I gotta backup plan."

Good-looking man, Toby's father, except when he wasn't smiling.

"You owe me, Okander. Getting tired of waiting."

Knowl took out a clean and folded handkerchief from his jacket and wiped his face just before he got back into that fancy car of his.

Early thought for sure D Jay'd have a go at him for goofing around with Toby, but he just watched Toby's old man drive away, then walked around in a circle, talking to himself. Got into his truck and sped off.

❋

Early worked long hours so D Jay wouldn't get sore. When the day was gone, he moved a lantern inside the shed, but it didn't look to be making much difference. The check marks on the back of the chicken shed said it was Saturday and there were no windows, no doors, no floor.

The harbour breeze felt cool as he sat against an unfinished wall, listening to the hum of a nearby heat bug. He saw the outline of a moored ship when the moon showed up. Houses 'round the turn and up the road had lights on, soft music playing on someone's radio.

"Hey, Early. You over there?" Toby was on the tracks with a lantern. "You gotta come with me."

Early stood and picked up his own light.

"They've got Grandpa's leg. My dad and your dad. They're playing cards in Miss Portia's place because you burned down the trailer and they've got all these men from town coming." Toby stopped. Breathe in, breathe out. "Mrs. Aada went over to say if Deacon English wasn't visiting in Cherry Brook he'd have something to say about this, but my dad kicked Ol' Nip to stop barking and told Mrs. Aada to get stuff from her store for them to eat. You gotta come, Early."

It'd be a whole lot faster going piggyback.

"Who's that? Who's down there on the tracks?"

"Me."

"Who's me?"

"Me and Toby, Mr. Sumlar."

"Early? You boys ought to be in bed, not playing on train tracks in the middle of the night. And I don't care for those chickens of yours keeping me up."

"Yes, sir."

At Aubrey's, cars were strewn everywhere. The door to Jubilee Hall was open, the music loud, and people were standing around having a smoke or going back and forth to Aubrey's shitter. Poor Mrs. Trilby. She wasn't happy. Inside the shed three tables were surrounded by men playing cards and smoking, passing jokes and bottles back and forth. D Jay and Knowl were in there too.

"And Mom," said Toby.

"They shouldn't be in there. That's for Miss Portia."

Toby took hold of Early's arm. "Let's go see Grandpa."

He was sitting at the kitchen table where Knowl and D Jay left him after taking the leg. Ol' Nip was on the floor. Good time to be almost deaf.

"How's Mrs. Aada?" he asked.

Early looked out the window. "Light off over there. Must be sleepin'."

"Not with that racket. Probably go on till dawn."

"Shouldn't be in there."

"Put the kettle on for me, then you boys get to bed."

"But you can't be doing nothing."

"I can hop across the kitchen and make myself a cup of tea. Now go."

Being hot out, the boys didn't close the bedroom window. Outside there was laughing, some yelling.

"Early, you pee already?"

"Yeah."

"You think Mrs. Aada's all right?"

Lights shone into the room, radio blaring. A car door slammed and someone walked by the window.

"Toby? You know who sings that song?" Early asked from his floor bed.

"Little Eva."

"Everybody's do-oo-ing the loco-motion."

"Shut up, Early. You've got the worst voice."

"Hey!"

Whoever was saying that was not on the radio. That got both of them sitting up, scrambling over to the window.

"It's me, Chub. Let me in."

"What are you doing?"

"Pull me inside and I'll tell you."

Early grabbed her under her arms and easily lifted her in her pyjamas and slippers inside the window. Scratching outside Toby's door meant Ol' Nip wanted in. He gave Chub a short bark and a hello sniff.

"Hey, boy."

Chub plunked down on the bed and fell back.

"You'll never guess. Tonight, my dad's supposed to be doing stuff with the Knights of Columbus. Aunt Joy's looking at apartments, and Derek, he wants to go next door to Eddie's and watch TV, but my dad said Mom's in bed so he's got to babysit me. All that yelling about who's staying to watch me and who's going got me so mad. You know what? They don't care about me and I don't need babysitting, so I hid in the back seat of our car where it's quiet and if they think I've been murdered, good. Let 'em think that. Guess I fell asleep 'cause I woke up bouncing on the road here. I know Dad'll be real mad if he finds me, so I stayed hidden till he got out."

Chub sat up.

"What's my dad doing here?"

"There's a poker game in Miss Portia's place," said Toby.

"How'd your grandpa let that happen?"

"Got his wooden leg so he couldn't say no."

"The Knights of Columbus wouldn't do that."

"My dad and D Jay did."

"Then why's my dad here?"

"Playin' cards?"

"No way. He must be lost and asking for directions."

"Cops never come down to check," said Toby. "No one'll know."

"Not my dad. Gambling's wrong. Says so in the Bible. At least I think it does."

Toby didn't say anything.

"You don't believe me?"

"If you think—"

"I'm going home."

Chub started crawling out the window, then fell back inside. She waved her hands and whispered, "C'mere."

Buddy standing in the doorway of Jubilee Hall was bald, shoulders right back, with a big wallet in his back pocket making one side of his arse even bigger. A big brown mole sat on his neck. Funny looking sort, reminded Early of a rooster, with his arm around a woman.

"Who's that?"

The man laughed because the woman didn't look too happy to be there, then he kissed her.

"It's my dad," said Chub.

Toby said he was really sorry for thinking Chub's old man had come down to gamble.

Chub sat on the floor. Early and Toby ducked as the couple passed by the window and got into the car.

Then D Jay followed after Knowl, saying D Jay's not getting his share because he screwed up on the shed being ready. That got D Jay fighting mad, like maybe he wanted to punch Knowl. D Jay was a good fighter, but Toby's dad, he was younger, better shape, once showed his son the gun he had. Didn't take much to get D Jay down on the ground. When a light went on next door at Mrs. Aada's, they stopped wrestling and D Jay said Knowl's gonna be really sorry and Toby's dad said bring it on whitey.

After that, Chub didn't feel like talking. None of them did. It was late, and the card game didn't sound like it was going to let up soon. No one would mind Toby and Early crawling out that window to walk Chub home.

Waking up on Sunday at Toby's meant smelling coffee getting fixed in the kitchen. At Aubrey's the rule was, coffee in the A.M., tea in the P.M. Sure was a good smell knowing the best part came after, when they'd go to Mrs. Aada's for breakfast. But Early didn't get up to coffee.

"Keep your mouth shut and don't wake 'em," D Jay said.

Early was still sleepy. Ol' Nip remembered getting kicked the night before, so he just looked at them from the kitchen as they slipped out the back door.

The tables inside Jubilee Hall were covered with bottles, cigarette burns scarred that nice wood floor. The outhouse lay on its side.

Early got into the truck like his pops wanted.

"Where we goin'?"

D Jay had one of those orange plastic cones on the seat beside him, like the ones they used on the road to keep cars from getting into tar or white paint.

"Why you got that?"

His pops said they were going to the trailer. Even though the trailer wasn't there anymore, he still said the trailer. When they got there, D Jay ordered Early out and to bring that road cone. D Jay picked up an axe from the pile of tools Early left behind and walked over to the shed.

"Why you goin' in there, Pops?"

All this chit-chat got the chickens going wild inside.

"Because it's your fault my trailer's gone and last night's game had to be somewhere else. That fuckin' skid mark cheated me out of my share, says I had nothing to do with runnin' things. So you listen to me, you mother fuckin' jellyfish, you're gonna sell those chickens for me by the side of the road. I'll teach you to mind me."

D Jay went into the shed. He came out with Evelyn, swinging her by her feet. He shoved her up through the cone so just her head was sticking out.

"Now cut it off."

"But it's Evelyn."

"It's a fuckin' chicken. Do it."

So Early did. There was a lot of blood, and when D Jay pulled Evelyn out of the cone, her feet and wings were still flapping. Inside the shed, the others knew what was coming.

D Jay made Early do Maud, Libby, then Flora and Mercy. Emily went last. There was blood on the ground, all over Early too.

D Jay jumped back into his truck, but not without leaving the orders. "Drain 'em, get the feathers off 'em, have 'em ready for when I get back."

The whirligig on Mr. Sumlar's house tinkled.

Toby wanted to know what happened, but Early couldn't hear for the buzzing in his ears. He was sitting against the shed. Next to him, the chickens, plucked like D Jay wanted.

His pops had been gone a long time.

The chickens looked like dead babies, except with no heads. Early saw a dead baby once. A midwife came all the way from Lucasville and took a baby from Damaris Symonds. Baby came out like those dead chickens.

They were covered in flies, making all the buzzing noise in Early's ears.

Toby said you got to get up Early, you gotta help me fix Grandpa's shitter.

The dried blood on Early's shirt felt like cardboard.

This time, it was Toby doing the carrying. Not really, Early being so big, but it was like he was getting Early to walk, telling him one foot in front of the other.

When they got to the church, folks coming out stopped talking. Deacon English asked what happened there, boys, and Toby jumped right in about the chickens. Blind Emmett wanted to know what everyone was going on about. Mrs. Jensen said Early's covered in blood, head to toe. Blind Emmett wished he could see that.

Aubrey was sweeping inside Jubilee Hall and waved the boys over. The church door was off its hinges. Daylight squeezed inside after them. Early liked the smell of wet cedar, tar, and rope along with horseshit and gasoline and damp earth that came from all the different wood.

Toby told his grandfather about the blood and the chickens.

"You okay, Early?"

He looked to Toby to find out if he was, then nodded.

Aubrey raised the broom up towards the gable over the door and unlatched the shutters. Light filtered through the ceiling sheathed with layers of coloured bottles, some painted with designs of gold, each one tied with a different length of string, its bottom cut off. A glass ceiling that quivered and chimed as each bottle gently tapped against the next.

"I guess Miss Portia'll never come now, eh, Grandpa?"

"Those boys didn't do nothing that can't be fixed."

"It's pretty bad."

"Nothing's ever that bad that you can't clean up from, son."

Aubrey scratched Ol' Nip's head as Early ran his hands over the bottles. Some were broken.

"You know, I married your grandmother when she was seventeen. Grew up with her. Lived right over there, same house Old Irene still lives in. Never married herself, that one. Think she'd rather have a life hating me over what I did to her sister."

Ol' Nip curled up in the middle of the floor, like maybe he'd heard most of this before.

"I wasn't much older than Maddie, nineteen. Know it now, too young to be married. Too young to bring a kid into this world. Your mom came along not long after. I know you won't believe this, but it was different here in Africville then. A real town of its own. City didn't mind us, dump wasn't there. Trains not so bad if you kept off the tracks. My mother still lived with us in this house my dad built, though she never got over losing him like she did. Guess me leaving Maddie is what caused your mom to grow so wild, although there were times, watching Deborah under the trees reading those books of hers that you like, she was the sweetest child. Could've made something of herself. Smart girl. Could've got away."

Early smiled as the bottles rushed together in the breeze from the shutters.

"First time I saw her, I was on the roof of the school, used to be by the church there, hammering shingles. Watched her walking along Campbell Road carrying a leather bag of books. Thin, scared bit of a girl come to teach. A real beauty. Got me falling for her, right off the roof, dislocated my shoulder. I was sure I'd made such a fool out of myself, took a year to say hello. But on a good day, windows open, hearing her sing in there with the kids, I knew. I knew. Sometimes, if you're lucky, you just do."

A plank bench with some greenish blue paint still on it was pushed against the roof beam in the centre of the shed. Must have been for times like now, when Aubrey wanted to take a load off that leg of his.

"'Course, Maddie and Deborah in the way, never set well with Miss Portia. And that singing of hers, like an angel, an angel right here in Africville, had people coming 'round for her. Wasn't long before we were listening to her on the radio. Real proud that day, but I tell you, saddest day of my life. Last time I saw her was just before the war. She was leaving on her first tour. A coloured girl, teaching in our school, singing for the world.

"So Toby, you get Early up to the house and clean him up, then go tell Mrs. Aada we need another broom."

THE CHICKENS HAD TO BE BURIED. DAYS HAD
gone by since D Jay said he'd be back for them. Early
wasn't sure, knowing how angry his pops'd get, but Toby
insisted. Gotta put them in the ground, Early. So he dug a
hole behind the shed and put them in, side by side, making
sure he got each one's head over the right body.

"You think chickens go to heaven?"

"Don't be soft."

Early sniffed.

"Ah, I'm sorry. Don't do that. Grandpa says he's not
going if Ol' Nip ain't there."

"That'd be like me and you, huh?"

Toby got a funny look on him.

"We'll be in different heavens, Early. You'll be in
Chub's."

Early thought about sitting outside the pearly gates
with Aubrey. Him missing that dog, Early missing Toby.

"So? Go fishing?"

"Better not. Pops'll be mad if he comes around."

"Can't work on a day you bury chickens."

Toby had a point. Besides, it was hot. Not a single well in Africville that didn't need its water boiled before drinking.

"Wanna get Chub?"

They hadn't seen her since her dad kissed that woman. That meant Chub didn't know about Early's girls losing their heads.

They started up the hill.

"Hey, Toby, trees are changin'."

Some of the maples were yellow and red around the edges. Early didn't like to think about being cold and deep snow. When they got over the upper tracks, they crawled into the irises and waited.

"What if she's not home?"

Her bike was, surrounded by the blue flowers. They were all done with blooming, except for the odd one here and there.

"She's gotta be home."

"Go knock on the door and see if she comes. It'll be okay if you go. And if she doesn't answer, run back."

Early crawled from under the red sumac and hurried to the door. Chub did answer.

"What are you doing here?"

Early talked fast in case her folks or that brother of hers or the lady next door saw him.

"Me and Toby are goin' fishin'."

Chub stepped onto the porch and had a look for Toby in the flowers. Early wondered about the dog next door. Chub waved Toby over, but Toby shook his head no.

"It's all right. C'mon."

Toby took a minute crossing the yard so he could look down on Africville.

"No one's home but me and Derek and he's upstairs listening to records. Everyone's at the hospital."

Because Chub's mom turned her ankle trying to get down the stairs with her walker.

"It was really bad. I was down in the basement doing laundry when it happened. You should have heard her, making these grunts as she fell, tangled up in that walker, her head hitting the stairs. I was so scared I almost squished my hand in the rollers on the washing machine. Good thing Derek was up in his room and he ran to get her. I heard him say that Mom peed herself."

"What did you do?"

Chub ran a finger up and down the screen in the door.

"It's not my fault she's sick. Her scraping up those floors she loves, spitting all over the place because she can't talk, and my dad hiding outside watering the lawn."

"It's okay, Chub."

"I stayed in the basement so Derek wouldn't think I was there."

Then when Chub heard the screen door slam—Derek calling for his Aunt Joy who was at Mrs. Venney's next door asking about jobs at city hall—she crawled up on her dad's workbench and got out through the basement window. She hid in the irises until the ambulance took her mom away.

"She okay?"

Chub nodded. "Your grandpa get his leg back?"

"Yeah. They knocked over the outhouse."

"Ew. Someone inside?"

"Dunno. Early set it back up."

"Good."

"You get in trouble for seeing your dad?"

Chub shook her head.

"You tell your mom about him and that other lady?"

"Shut up about that."

Early sat on the step beside Chub, Toby on the other side.

"So, wanna come fishing?"

"Can't. I'm being punished."

"Thought you said no one saw you?"

"By God, silly. He sees everything. Mom told me, bad things'd happen if I went down there." With her chin, she nodded towards the harbour. "It's true. All this bad stuff is my fault."

Chub kicked the step with her sneaker.

Early wanted to know what happened when you got punished by God.

"He makes you feel sick until you say you're sorry. But I can't do that. Means I have to ask to go to confession and wear a dress and black shiny shoes. Mom'll want to know why. Just wish there's a way I could get the sorry part done without anyone knowing. Except God."

"Deacon English says baptizing in our church washes away sin."

"Thought you had to be twelve?"

"Close enough."

"How do we do it?"

Toby gave it some thought.

"You need something white to wear. Then we'll dunk you and I'll say a prayer from the Bible."

Early said, "Yeah, we'll dunk you."

"Wait."

Chub jumped up and disappeared inside. She came back with an old bedsheet and a pair of scissors.

"It's got some blue flowers on it, but maybe God won't see that under water."

Early said it was practically white.

Chub pulled the sheet over her head and gave Toby the scissors. He cut holes for her head and hands.

"You think if I get baptized, all this bad stuff'll stop?"

"Can't say for sure, but it'll be okay for you to come fishing after you're sorry."

They walked down the hill, Early first, Toby, then Chub wearing her sheet. When they got to the shed, Early was glad Toby didn't say Early's dad made him cut the chickens' heads off, because that would have made Chub sadder than she was.

At the shore, Chub and Early climbed onto the rocks and waited for Toby. He ran over to the church.

"I got it," he said coming back, waving the book over his head.

"So? What do I do?"

"Go stand in the water. You too, Early."

"It's cold."

"Now Early, dunk Chub in. Make sure she's all wet, and I'll read."

"What about singing?"

"I can do that."

"Shut up, Early. You sure can't sing."

Chub had them wait while she crossed her arms over her chest and closed her eyes.

"Okay, now."

Early dropped her into the water and sure, it was cold, but Chub came up screaming and coughing, ran onto shore, and tore that wet sheet off.

"Something grabbed me."

"You messing with her, Early?"

"No, Toby, I mean it. Something grabbed my leg."

Early stuck his head into the water. It was pretty murky even though it wasn't deep. That's when he saw the eyes. Got him on land beside Chub damn quick.

"What is it?"

"I dunno. Somethin' lookin' at me."

"Better tell."

Early ran up the road, past the church. Deacon English came to mind, living next door to Aubrey and Mrs. Aada, right next to the road and the tracks. Lucky guy. Could lean out his window and wave to the trains.

Early knocked on his door like crazy and when Deacon English came to say what, Early jumped right in with him and Toby and Chub doing baptizing down by the water because Chub's sorry to God and something grabbed onto Chub and when Early looked he saw eyes down there.

"Settle down, Early. What are you going on about?" Deacon English had his shirt collar open and his sleeves rolled up.

"Like I said."

"You find a body on the shore?"

A nod.

"What colour?"

He didn't know. It was dark down there, but maybe it was white and Early said so.

When Deacon English and Early got back to Toby and Chub, they were standing on the shore pointing because whatever was down there was floating back up. Deacon English waded in for a look.

"It's nothing but a dead seal."

"Can we see?"

"No, it's rotting some. Probably full of disease. Toby, run along to your grandfather's place, right now. Early, get down here and help me. We got to drag this thing out deep so it'll sink."

"But we wanna see."

"Go."

So they did, Chub grumbling about it being not fair and why couldn't they see the dead seal. She wished she had her camera now.

"Early, get down here."

When he did, Early saw that Deacon English wasn't telling the truth.

"That's no seal."

But the man was banged up, not much left of the face

except for the eyes staring, mouth wide open. No telling who he was, other than he was white. Early tried to back away, but Deacon English took hold of his arm, real tight, and held on.

"Looks like the poor beggar's been beaten."

"Killed?"

"Early, listen to me. You got that raft you and Toby get out on?"

Early nodded.

"Go get it."

"What for?"

"Don't you be asking me that, just do what I say."

Early'd never heard the deacon speak like D Jay, so he ran for his raft.

"You gotta drag this away from here. If he gets found near Africville, the police'll come. You don't want that, do you? You don't want anything bad to happen to Toby and his grandfather and Mrs. Aada?"

"Why would somethin' bad happen?"

"It just will, that's all."

Deacon English took off his belt and tied the body to the raft. Then he took a look at the sky.

"Getting dark. Good. Now get this raft as far down the shore as you can, all the way to the pier. Let him go there. The tide'll take him out. And Early, when you get back, don't you say anything to anybody. You hear me?"

"Not even to Toby?"

"Not even to him. If he asks, it's like I said, a dead seal. You got that?"

"But that's lyin'."

Deacon English took a deep breath. A real deep one.

"It's a white lie, Early. They're good ones. They help people. You want to help Toby, don't you?"

"Sure."

"So no one must know about this."

"Okay."

"You don't want to get into trouble, right?"

"No."

"You don't want the police to come and take you away? They will if you tell."

"No."

Then he could help Deacon English push the raft off the sandy bottom. The deacon waded to shore where he wiped his hands with his handkerchief. He got smaller and smaller until Early was far enough away to see all of Africville in evening grey lit by squares of light. Boys on the train tracks tossed a ball back and forth. Early had to get back to make sure the chickens were penned for the night. Oh. Might take some getting used to, this not being needed. Early thought maybe he'd pile rocks on the chickens' graves in case the raccoons came back.

When he was far enough off shore, Early sat and let the breeze slowly spin the raft around. He shivered. The floating man's boots tapped against the wood. Voices from the pier bounced across the water, not so you could understand, just so you could hear. He remembered D Jay taking him there once, when he was very small. The sounds of the machines scared him and he cried, so D Jay bought him some ice cream. Chocolate. Early smiled, then he remembered that he'd gotten it wrong. Aubrey gave him the ice cream.

When it was dark, Early thought he should say a prayer, but all he could remember was something from Mrs. Aada about laying me down to sleep and the Lord taking souls, and from Aubrey, sleep tight and don't let the bedbugs bite. Then he did like Deacon English said. Got rid of the dead seal.

AUBREY ASKED EARLY TO GET THE KEROSENE
lamp from the back porch and put it on the kitchen table
for Chub.

"Sure is nice of you to be writing these letters for me,"
Aubrey said. "My eyes aren't so good with the light this
time of day."

Mrs. Aada knew who to blame for that. "It's because you
didn't pay your electric bill again thanks to Early eating
you out of those few dollars the government gives you each
month for losing your leg."

"It was my leg, missus, so I figure it's up to me how I
spend the money. I need that boy to help me with Jubilee
Hall. You're welcome here, Early, and don't you forget it."

"Have you seen the pants on him? Good thing it's
summer and he can go around barefoot, or we'd have to
be worrying about shoes too. And no thanks to that D Jay
coming around to look after his boy."

Early was sitting by the stove with Ol' Nip's head in his

lap. From there he saw Chub and Toby look at each other across the table and smile.

"Why don't you let Toby write those letters for you? It's not like she needs the practice."

"Toby's a leftie, Mrs. Aada," said Chub. "He'll smudge these letters to Miss Portia."

"Thank you, dear. I had no idea about Toby being left-handed."

Mrs. Aada went back to wiping the spots of cream off the counter. She said it was everywhere and since Aubrey made the mess, he should clean it.

"I told you, you can't whip cream when it's cloudy. Might as well make butter."

"Old wives' tale." Aubrey wanted whipped cream on that apple pie Mrs. Aada made and there was plenty from Mrs. Trilby.

Chub said they had one of those hand beaters at home like Aubrey tried to use, but her arms got really sore using it.

Aubrey put on his hat and thought he might walk over to Miss Ruby's for a stamp and a bit of peace. "You know, I think she must be losing mail. I should've had a letter by now."

"No way, no how, is that woman coming here to sing— not after singing for the Queen. You might as well walk down to the water and drop the letter in there."

"You got that one just about ready, Chub?"

After so many letters, Mrs. Aada wanted to know what was left to say?

Chub said plenty, like how much folks in Africville still remember her teaching and how there was a fancy place for her to sing. Got seats from an old movie theatre in it, and Early fixed it up nice. If she came in summer, it was real pretty down by the harbour, but she'd remember that from before. She had lots of fans, no one bigger than Aubrey Daye. Always signed, respectfully.

"Thank you, Chub. That's another fine job. Maybe they'll be something waiting for me this time."

Mrs. Aada watched him go from the kitchen window.

Chub whispered to Toby, "You think they'll get a divorce?"

"Who?" Mrs. Aada dropped the curtain.

"You and Toby's grandpa."

"Honey, we're not married. And that's a grown-up word."

"I hear it all the time at home. They think me and Derek don't know things, but if you put your head against the vent upstairs, you can hear lots."

"You shouldn't be listening."

"Not my fault. Mom being sick and moving vans bringing stuff for Aunt Joy. She's getting a divorce because all she and my Uncle Ernie do is fight on the telephone. It's true. I hear them."

"Toby's grandfather, well, me and him, we're not fighting."

"What's a divorce?"

"Early, it's a mortal sin. My Aunt Joy and Uncle Ernie'll go to hell. Forever."

Toby's parents didn't live together. Did that mean they were going too?

"Oh, no. They're not like us. We're Catholics. We've got different rules."

"You kids shouldn't be talking about other people's misery."

"Just my aunt, Mrs. Aada. She's going to lose her house on Island Park Drive, the one next door to some man who owns a swanky store. My Uncle Ernie's been stealing money from Coca-Cola to keep his girlfriend and baby in an apartment. Now the police know. Toby, what if my parents get a divorce?"

There was that kiss.

"Maybe that's how my Uncle Ernie started off, kissing women he shouldn't be."

"You like your dad, huh?"

"I guess. He's just my dad. Mostly he doesn't say much to me, but Derek, he's always yelling at him. Says how come he's putting pictures of guys on TV up on his walls. You think my dad might catch what happened to Aunt Joy, you know, like a cold?"

Early couldn't say, but Toby didn't think you could catch a divorce.

"I just wish she'd hurry up and move out."

Chub said she was looking for a trailer in a park somewhere nearby to start over.

Early thought Chub liked her aunt. Why did she want her to move? Didn't she say her Aunt Joy put vanilla ice cream in her cola and called it a float, even cooked her own soap, and sometimes made a chocolate liqueur that Chub got to taste?

"Lots of reasons, and Mrs. Venney got her a job typing at city hall, working for the planner who wants to put factories here."

"Where?"

"Here, in Africville."

"On top of us?"

"No, stupid. They think this is a slum and the city's all shamed by it now because we're supposed to be modern. Aunt Joy won't shut up about putting you guys in houses with toilets."

Chub put her hand on Toby's.

"But don't worry. Some people are trying to stir up trouble and make you stay."

Aubrey didn't have much to say about all this when he came back in and hung up his hat. No letter.

"Moving? Heard that before. No different now."

Mrs. Aada knew about a big city lawyer getting together with a human rights council, but from what she heard, most of the folks on it weren't even from Africville and they were going to speak for the community? Make decisions? No indeed, thank you very much.

"But that day is coming, Aubrey. I've been here all my life just like you, and the city is still going to throw us off our land, mind my words."

Then she told the kids to get out of the house. Mrs. Aada said writing letters with such fine weather outside was an affront to God. There'd be enough time for that when school started in a few weeks. That'd be for Chub and Toby, not Early. Besides, Aubrey had no business taking up Chub's time. Miss Portia was never going to come and sing in Africville and if the good Lord lost His mind and willed it so, by time she got here, they'd be all gone anyhow.

*≺

Early and Aubrey, Toby and Chub and Ol' Nip were on the lane by Mrs. Aada's house. A broken fence with tall grass poking through ran alongside it to Aubrey's, then around Deacon English's place and up to the main road that went by the church and took them to Miss Ruby's.

Hard to say if Miss Ruby was older than Mrs. Aada, but she was certainly old and still a Miss. Always had a joke, like why'd the chicken cross the road? Miss Ruby, Grandpa's own pa told him that one, but Early didn't mind if it had been told before. Miss Ruby always had gumdrops in a bowl to help yourself.

Aubrey had his face bent to the sky and was saying not too many fine days like this left after they headed into September. Night already getting a chill to it. Ol' Nip was looking up too, or maybe just smelling a horsefly. That's when they noticed the car coming over the train tracks, kicking up dust, bouncing up and down over the dirt road's potholes.

First thing that came to Early: that's D Jay. He drove like that, but Toby, he remembered better.

"Chub, that's your car."

No time to say more. The car slammed to a stop. Chub had to scoop up Ol' Nip or he'd have been squashed for sure. Inside, there was a woman, tiny thing, big eyes, staring at them like maybe they were standing there naked. She locked the door.

Chub's dad stepped out.

"Get in."

"But Dad, I'm with my friend Toby—"

"You hear me? Get in."

A vein in the man's neck popped right out underneath that mole. Only Chub got the mean look, like the rest of them weren't even there. Didn't give Chub a chance to say what for. Came around the front of the car and grabbed her arm. Chub had to dump poor Ol' Nip into Early's lap. Her dad had to bang on the window and tell the woman inside to open the god-damned car because she locked his door too as soon as he got out. Then Chub got in the back seat and they drove away.

Living with Toby and Aubrey, Early didn't have to check the days off anymore on the back of the shed. They told him when hallelujah day was. He'd still walk out to his shed to check on the chickens, but when he got there he'd remember, oh yeah. So he was trying now to remember how many sleeps it was since they'd seen Chub.

Toby wasn't doing so well. He was kinda quiet during the days, tossing around a lot at night. Mrs. Aada thought Toby must've got something. She saw that skin of his peeling. Never said he missed Chub, but Early knew he did. After Chub's father had taken her, no one expected her to ever come back, but maybe all Toby needed was to know that she was okay. So when Toby finally did get to sleep, Early crawled out the window.

He saw a deer once in those woods behind D Jay's shed. Lots of rabbits, anytime. Early didn't mind crawling up through there during the day, but at night, real late, it was a good place for fellas to flash the headlights on their cars, shoot at rats running across the road. Then maybe they'd have a drink, a smoke, get mean to boys like Early. The ones that smelled of aftershave and gave him tips, like Mr. Navy, could follow him into his dreams, and then Early'd have to get up and wash his sheets. But tonight only stars were out.

Dead quiet up there on the top of the hill. The sumac was dropping red leaves on the browned-up irises. None of the houses had lights on. Early had to wait for a long time, getting sleepy, before a light went on in Chub's room, a shadow going back and forth behind the blind. She looked like a black cut-out doll on account of the light being behind her, but she seemed to have all her arms and legs. Toby'd be pleased.

When the dog started barking next door at Mrs. Venney's, Early ran.

AUBREY KEPT LOOKING OUT THE WINDOW AS HE stirred around the eggs in the frying pan, then he laid out clean pants and a shirt for Toby's first day back at school. Polished his shoes too. Deborah wasn't coming by with money for new clothes, like she said, so the old stuff ironed by Mrs. Aada had to do for new. Toby didn't mind. Couldn't wait to get out the door.

Toby said this year school was going to be the best. He was even happy about going back to the dumb class. That's because Toby wasn't planning on staying in it. This year Chub was going to help him get A's.

"I know you'll be sad, Early, me not being around during the day, but that's because I'll be with Chub and she'll be helping me learn. If you wait by the school, you can visit with her too."

Other kids in pants that didn't have patches, carrying shiny book bags, were making a game of jumping in the road puddles to break the ice outside of Deacon English's house. He was in the yard rubbing his hands. Winter looked to be a long one when ice came before the leaves were down. Maybe the early frost'd kill those caterpillars that ate his tree every year.

"Never saw ice before school started."

"Strange for sure, Toby."

They started walking along the tracks.

"Know what, Early? Lots of strange things been happening. Mrs. Aada said she doesn't think she'll be selling stuff in the store anymore."

No more Cherry Blossoms?

"And Larry Ganes should have his dad's Christmas lights up by now, before he goes back to university so he's not climbing up a ladder in a snow squall so thick you can't see your nose."

Toby reached up and pinched Early's nose. Early laughed.

Strangest of all, Molasses Jack left his house covered in boards so boys like Charlie Savage and Tom Reed couldn't break the windows.

"Mrs. Aada said the city was going to get him out anyhow so he got himself a place in Mulgrave Park."

Heading into school, Toby had a smile on his face like it wanted to burst out, but Toby kept his mouth shut real tight so it didn't get away on him.

"Don't you be missing me, Early."

He'd be back before Early knew it, maybe even with Chub for a bit of playing by the pond.

"Okay," said Early.

Good thing there was work to be done finishing off

Jubilee Hall, and D Jay'd be some mad if his shed didn't have a roof when he finally came 'round. Maybe Early wouldn't miss Toby so much, fixing up here, fixing up there, looking down the road, wondering when school was out.

In the afternoon, Aubrey and Ol' Nip came to see Early. Skies were looking cloudy and Aubrey didn't want Toby getting caught in the rain. Aubrey gave Early the umbrella, said he should go wait. School ought to be finished soon. The rain only waited until Early got across the tracks, and it didn't take much to turn the road to mud. Early didn't use the umbrella. He saved that for Toby.

It was pouring when Early got to the Richmond School. Toby had that drowned cat look. Sometimes they get washed up from the harbour. Look more skinny when their fur's sticking to them. Why didn't Toby wait inside? He didn't want to. And he must have given away that smile he was trying to keep to himself in the morning.

Early opened the umbrella he'd been saving.

"Forget it, Early."

Wasn't going to do either of them much good, seeing as how they were wet right into their underwear.

"Chub comin'?"

"She's not going to school here anymore."

Didn't seem like Toby wanted to talk much after that, so he didn't, all the way back on the muddy road.

Mrs. Aada gave a bit of a do that night to celebrate Toby's school day. She even made strawberry shortcake with preserves from the berries Early and Toby picked on Uncle Laffy's Hill back in June. Early thought his eyes'd pop out of his head when he saw the mounds of whipped cream coming thanks to Mrs. Trilby, but Toby, he pushed his bowl over. You eat this, Early. That meant lots on account of Chub not coming by to help.

The rain worsened, and Aubrey placed pots around the kitchen and stuck towels along the windowsills.

"Better get up on the roof, Early, and lay out that plastic sheet or nobody's going to get any sleep with all this dripping."

Toby wanted to help, but his grandpa reminded him he'd had his bath, meaning, getting wet on the way home. So had Early, and he was already using his only other dry clothes, so before he went out, he took off his shirt and pants and left them folded by the door.

Putting that piece of plastic over the kitchen roof took some doing up there in the dark and rain. But easy enough for someone used to slinging a tarp over a trailer. That was when Early noticed the car, coming real slow, like whoever inside was looking for a place. It stopped by his ladder, but nobody got out. The car was still idling with the headlights on when Early climbed down.

"That you, Early?" said a woman in fancy rain gear, getting out of the car.

He couldn't see her face, but he knew her, Toby's mom, by the sound of her. She waved and the car drove off.

"What are you doing up there looking like that?"

"So the rain don't get in."

"Jesus." Deborah got her hand wiping the rain from Early's shoulders and chest. "You are some good looking, Early. Got a sweetheart telling you that?"

He didn't get a chance to say, because Deborah took his hand and pulled him around back of Jubilee Hall. Mrs. Trilby was there, eating grass, she was always eating grass, but she didn't look too happy about the rain.

"Toby and his grandpa's inside."

Deborah didn't care about them just then. She pushed Early against the wall and ran her fingers down his chest and into his briefs.

"You're all grown up, eh, Early? What's this? You like what I'm doing?"

His hands rolled into fists all by themselves. She smelled different from Mr. Navy.

"Oh, I'm just messing with you, kid. Finish yourself off out here. You can't come in with that thing all raring to go."

Deborah went inside, leaving Early with the cow.

"Don't you be watching," he said to Mrs. Trilby.

When Early got back inside, that sweet voice of Deborah's wasn't singing. She'd noticed the pink patches on Toby when she gave him a hug. Now the T-shirt was off, and she was yanking him around in front of her, checking him over. Early didn't care for the way Toby's head was bobbing around.

"Dad, look at him."

"He got a lot of sun this summer. That's all."

"That's not sunburn. You get him to a doctor?"

"You know I don't have money for that."

"Christ, not that again."

"Deborah, do you have to talk like that?"

She tossed the shirt back at Toby and told him to get out of her sight. Early too. That left Aubrey and his daughter fighting in the kitchen, not with hands or anything, but with words. Seemed to Early just as bad. It was over when Aubrey said all he's got is ten dollars and maybe some change.

Inside their room, Toby dove onto the bed and rolled over to the wall so Early couldn't see his face.

"Thanks for not telling."

"Yeah."

"I'm not going to stop, you know."

"Okay."

Deborah rapped softly on the door, but didn't open it. She was sorry she couldn't stay longer and promised she would next time. The house got quiet after she left.

"Toby?"

"Yeah?"

"Why you do it?"

"Because they don't put white kids in the dumb class." Then Toby said, "Go to sleep."

TOBY MADE A PLAN TO SEE CHUB. FIRST, HE ASKED
Aubrey how far it was to Spring Garden Road because
they'd been talking about it in class. That was where
Chub's new school was, but Toby didn't let on because he
knew what his grandpa'd say about visiting.

Spring Garden Road? A man needed a pocket full of
change to take the bus, or two strong legs, because that was
the only way to get there unless you had wings.

That meant Early had to wait with the wagon for Toby
around the corner from his school, in front of St. Mark's.
Big church, brick. Make sure nobody sees you, Toby
whispered at breakfast. And no telling anyone about the
plan. Not Aubrey. Not Mrs. Aada. Toby was going to school
where he'd get pretend sick, and he'd have to put up his
hand and ask to go home please. Since he got sick a lot with
the asthma, no one'd even care.

"Told ya it'd work," he said, running along the sidewalk
when it did.

Toby had that big smile he got sometimes, like the one Early got inside when he knew they were going to be together.

"Anyone see you?"

Early shook his head, ear to ear.

"I've been up town lots with my dad. We drove in his car all over Halifax. Sometimes he even takes me for ice cream, so I'm sure I'll find it."

Early couldn't remember that. Funny thing, the longer they walked, that wagon in tow, Toby started looking around as if everything was brand new. Early recognized the road to the navy at Stadacona and the way to Mr. Welford's garage, but once past the memories of good times with Ben, it was all Greek to him.

"Why say that?"

"Ben says it when he don't get somethin'."

Toby laughed, and figured he'd better ask someone.

First person they said pardon me to was a lady coming out of a diner with her fish and chips wrapped in a brown bag. Reminded Early about getting hungry. Before they could ask for directions, the lady said she didn't have money for beggars, then she ran across the street.

"Oh well, keep going."

Toby made Early stop at the North Street intersection to take a long look at the bridge crossing the harbour. Even though it was at the end of the street, they could see its towers holding up the cables, and the road, over a passing tanker.

"Where do you think it's coming from?"

Early thought Jamaica on account of Molasses Jack and that being the only away place, apart from heaven, he could think of.

"I'm going to drive a car right across that bridge, when I get one."

"Me too?"

"Sure, Early. You'll be in the front seat with me."

Sometimes Early pulled Toby, sometimes Toby got out and walked. Trucks rumbled up and down the road because of all the buildings being torn down on Jacob Street. Some of those houses looked so old and slanty, Early bet Toby he could push one over and Toby said bet you could too. But maybe someone was still inside, and they didn't want to get in trouble.

"Early, you noticing anything about my grandpa and Mrs. Aada?"

"Like what?"

"Remember when that preacher came and told everyone he could make Blind Emmett see, and Blind Emmett ordered a bunch of flower seeds right away to put in his garden?"

Early said yes to remembering even when he couldn't so Toby wouldn't think him troublesome.

"Grandpa and Mrs. Aada are like Blind Emmett was after he didn't get to see, and he took those seeds and put them down the hole in his outhouse."

A man came out of the Saks store, and Toby asked where Spring Garden Road was. This fellow didn't think they wanted money, but he did ask how come they weren't in school. Then he pointed to the old citadel where soldiers in bear hats used to guard and said the street they were looking for was on the other side.

"Grandpa wasn't fooling," Toby said to Early. "Sure is a lot of walking."

Toby got back in the wagon and after they got around Citadel Hill, Toby helping to read the street signs, things brightened right up. Just like it was told to them, Spring Garden Road. That fancy school of Chub's was way down at the other end. Early didn't mind though. The street was full of cars and buses, sidewalks had lots of folks going places in a hurry missing all the neat stuff he saw in the windows.

Sacred Heart. Toby read that on the sign.

"Looks like a castle."

Except the castle had a fancy porch and a round driveway for cars instead of a drawbridge. Trees covered in yellow with orange bits surrounded brick walls and high windows. Right over the top of the place were cones, green and covered with bird shit and over that, a cross. Getting his eyes to come back down from looking up there, Early saw some fella made of metal blessing them from behind a black gate.

"How do we find Chub?"

"They got to have a recess or lunch. Maybe she'll come out to play and we can see her."

The idea of lunch got Early thinking just as a police car pulled alongside the sidewalk.

"What are you boys doing?"

"I'm waiting for my friend," said Toby.

"Where?"

"In there."

Early didn't know what was funny about that, but the policeman laughed.

"Move it before I take you in for being truant." Off he went, still laughing.

They didn't walk all this way just to go home. Hey, there was a park right across the street. Good place as any to wait, watch for Chub.

"Won't we get caught?"

"No, Early, see that? It says Public Gardens. That means free."

In that free garden, along the fence, was a row of rhododendron bushes, real big, like maybe they were a hundred years old, growing under giant elms, maybe two hundred years old. Toby said trees weren't like people, so maybe they were that old. Tucked in among them, out of the sun, they could watch the schoolyard across the street. Early pulled the wagon into the leaves, right against the fence.

Seemed like they waited forever, only because watching the ducks eat bread crumbs made Early's stomach growl.

"There she is."

Girls were coming out of the castle door, but how did Toby know which one was Chub? They were all dressed the same, laughing and joking, some in groups, some running back and forth.

"She's the one with short hair."

The one by herself, leaning against the black fence keeping those girls in and everyone else out.

"Hey."

Boy, she was some surprised.

"What are you doing here?"

Now, same big smile on her face Early'd seen on Toby's.

"We came to see you."

"Walked the whole way?"

"Mostly. Sometimes Early pulled me."

"How's your grandpa and Mrs. Aada and Mrs. Trilby? Are you milking her, Early? Your dad come back? What about Ol' Nip, still barking?" Then she remembered. "Better not come in here."

They all gave the problem some thought, mostly Chub and Toby, and decided where they were was best. Early pulled the wagon against the gate, and he and Toby sat in it while Chub crossed her legs on the grass on the other side.

"I hate these dumb skirts we have to wear, and I don't care if my panties show."

"This sure is better than Richmond School. Can I come here someday?"

"It's for girls only. And you'd hate the nuns. They're mean old cunts."

Early wanted to know what a nun was and Toby asked about cunts.

"Nuns get married to Jesus or something and give up having babies and you have to say yes sister no sister, and I heard Derek tell Eddie that girls have cunts. So I guess nuns got 'em."

"You make any friends yet?"

Chub looked over her shoulder.

"Girls here are stuck up. There's one girl, Leeza Jasmine, she's in my class. She laughs at me and says I have short hair like a boy. Calls me rug muncher."

"What's that?"

Chub didn't know.

Early knew that he was hungry.

"You got something to eat?"

Toby shook his head and Early said no.

"Hey, I know. Isabel's is around the corner. It's got a fat lady doing the twist on the sign. My dad took me there on my first day of school."

Toby didn't think going to a restaurant was a good idea.

"It'll be okay, you'll see."

"You coming?"

"Gonna sneak out the back so I don't get caught. There's a place by the school where the fence ends." Chub laughed. "Those big girls think they're so high and mighty 'cause they got tits. I'd like to see them squeeze through it."

Early and Toby watched as Chub ran around the back of the school. She met up with them on the other side of the block, old houses made into flats, Isabel's Café in the basement of one of them with a window looking out at the walk. Early wanted to know if they thought D Jay'd let him go inside and could he leave the wagon on the sidewalk.

"Sure, Early, no one'll take it."

They took seats at the counter, Early excited about being back in a diner, like him and Ben.

"Neat, huh?" said Chub. "It's a restaurant downstairs."

Early's stool wobbled and there were burn marks on the counter in front of him. Next to his elbow was a half-cut lemon pie under glass. A fly was stuck in the meringue.

"I don't have any money," Toby said, quiet like, so no one heard.

Chub did, sort of. Bus fare. The same bus Leeza took to get home, meaning Chub walked.

"We could get one thing and share."

That's when Isabel came over. At least, Early thought that's what her name was. Snarly thing, she didn't say. Short and broad, her long hair netted up behind her, Isabel's face looked glazed like one of Mrs. Aada's Easter hams and she acted like she was beautiful in low shoes and a button-up smock that was kind of stiff from old stains.

She pointed to the sign over the register and read: *No shirts, no shoes, no service. No exceptions.*

Chub and Toby looked to see if Early had shoes.

The woman tapped the sign with the pencil in her hand.

Lightly inked underneath in blocky letters, *NO COLOUREDS.*

Early tried to sound out the letters, but Toby didn't look happy when he did.

"I know. We can do like when my dad takes me and Derek to the Legion for Cokes. We'll sit in the booth by the window. You can be right outside on the sidewalk, Toby."

Isabel wanted to know if she should call one of the four

guys in the corner booth eating from platters of burgers and spilling fries on the table to help Toby outside.

Early slid into the booth, Chub too, and opened the window. Toby went up on the sidewalk and slouched against the foundation wall. Chub ordered a shake. They let Toby pick strawberry.

"Think you're smart, don't you?" Isabel said when she put the shake and three straws down on the table. She meant about Toby, with a nod of her head.

First Chub took a sip, then she handed the glass out the window to Toby, then Early had his turn. Early thought it was fun, but Toby's happiness had rubbed off and didn't come back.

"Hey, I forgot."

Chub pulled half a chocolate chip cookie her brother made from her pocket, but it was broken mostly into crumbs. She passed them to Early.

"Your brother makes cookies?"

"Yup. Mom can't anymore and Aunt Joy's too busy working, so Derek makes stuff now. Dad says baking's gonna turn Derek into a pansy."

"What's that?"

Chub shrugged.

They were the best damned cookie pieces Early ever had. Not counting what Mrs. Aada made.

Isabel called over that only food bought in the diner could be eaten in the diner.

Chub shrugged.

"You coming again tomorrow?"

"Dunno. It's far."

"Yeah, I guess. Mostly Dad picks me up, or else I'm supposed to take the bus."

"By yourself?"

"Sure. Why not? I'd be better off stolen by gypsies."

"Yeah?"

"I'm just joking. But I wish I could run away with gypsies, or a circus. "

Chub said her house was falling apart. Her mom wasn't walking much anymore even with her ankle better and Aunt Joy living there, and she told Derek about her dad playing poker in Africville. Chub said her big-mouth brother went and told. Good thing she never said anything about that woman he kissed. Her dad went out and got drunk and when he came home he was all I'm sorry I'm sorry, Lorette, and pissed in the corner of the living room because he thought it was the bathroom.

"They care more about Derek getting sick again with the pneumonia than me. And my Aunt Joy's best friends now with Mrs. Venney 'cause they work together, so Mikki thinks we'll be cousins. No way. I wish she'd go back to Newfoundland. That Aurora, she won't. She's saving to go to Italy and get married. She even showed me some fancy glass bowl her boyfriend sent because his family makes them over there. They blow it. I like her. She's got white go-go boots, too. Hey, you go to those meetings?"

"What meetings?"

"Aunt Joy says they've been having meetings in your church, about giving money to everyone to move."

Toby didn't like the sound of that.

"It's true. Another one next week. My aunt types stuff about them for the city hall."

"Mrs. Trilby get money too?"

"Shut up, Early."

Chub didn't get a chance to say. Isabel stood over them with the bill.

"Guess I should get back inside before the nuns catch me. Thanks for coming,"

Toby wanted to know who the girl was, staring at them.

"Stupid ugly Leeza."

Chub told them to ignore her and maybe she'd turn into a toad. No chance. Leeza was already running to the school porch, arms waving. She got a woman looking like she'd been dipped in chocolate at the Dairy Queen to come out calling, Penny Deforest, you get away from those boys right this minute. Real anxious sounding. Same time, the police car came back, stopped across the street.

"Better go."

Toby sat in the wagon and didn't look back, but Early did, in time to see that old cunt pry Chub's hands off the fence and drag her back across the grass.

Toby said Early probably shouldn't call her that.

CHUB WAS RIGHT ABOUT THOSE MEETINGS. MRS. Aada knew all about them too. She got fired up and kept saying what she was hearing coming from them wasn't good. Aubrey wasn't worried. There'd been talk, and meetings, lots of times before.

Mrs. Aada said Aubrey keeping his head in the sand was because of Miss Portia White and had gone on long enough. Voice of an angel, coming to save the day. Well, where was she? Mrs. Aada didn't sound like an angel, that's for sure. Sometimes even Ol' Nip got a bark in when things between Mrs. Aada and Aubrey really got to going.

"I can't believe you're going to sit back and let some highfalutin-sounding Human Rights Advisory Committee speak for us. Lived here all my life and I've never seen most of those do-gooders taking up the front rows of the church at those meetings. As for the white folks, no need to tell you, Aubrey Daye, I haven't seen them either. Nothing worse than do-gooders, especially when they're doing good in other folks' business."

Aubrey finally did get himself down to one of those meetings at the church only because he told Toby and Early that there'd be no peace and quiet from you-know-who until he did. So when Mrs. Aada showed up, Sunday hat and gloves ready, a few days after Toby and Early got back from visiting Chub, there was Aubrey putting on his jacket.

"You think they'll have singing there tonight?"

"Don't be so foolish. It's a meeting with folks from the city hall. Expect some fancy footwork, maybe."

"No singing, then?"

Toby'd gotten real sick after seeing Chub. Like his bones had gone to water and couldn't hold him up anymore. Early tried to get him outside, not so much for swimming anymore, it getting too cold for that, but maybe for a walk, carried on his shoulders. Naw, he wasn't interested. Seeing Mrs. Aada and Aubrey getting all smartened up for the meeting made him change his mind. Made Early happy. It was a real nice evening, much too nice to be sitting inside even though Mrs. Aada said they could watch her TV and *Petticoat Junction* was on. Early always laughed when he saw those girls swimming in the water tank. He wondered if they ever peed in there like he did sometimes at the beach.

Looked like a few other folks were heading to the church with them and Ol' Nip. Even Blind Emmett. Aubrey's dog barked hello and Blind Emmett barked back because he told Early he could talk dog better than anyone in Africville. He never missed anything going on in town.

Miss Ruby Hall either. She told them, after hello, that she had to come to these meetings, being postmistress and all, to know what was going on. Mrs. Aada said underneath a cough that was so she could tell tales afterwards.

"Coming in?"

No place for dogs and if Toby got fidgety, Mrs. Aada wouldn't be able to hear the men from the city speak.

"Pops don't want me in there."

"Do the likes of your father the world of good to step inside a church, Early Okander. Maybe then he wouldn't run off and leave you."

"I'll sit out here with Early and Ol' Nip," said Toby.

After Mrs. Aada and Aubrey went inside, a car came along, parked beside some of the others, and a man and a woman got out. Never saw the man before, but that woman? The man, he looked all important with a jacket and tie, hair greased back, said hello boys, passing by on the stairs. The woman had a pinched, scared look about her. Big eyes, curly hair, she said something about how in the name of all things holy could people be allowed to live like this. She called the man Mr. Wallace while she stared at Ol' Nip and wondered if that was the damned dog that barked all night. Early said hello. No more folks came after them.

"You okay out here, Early? You want to go inside and listen?"

No way. Sitting out here watching the day end with Toby, didn't get any better.

"Who's that?"

Some kid was coming down the road carrying a brown paper bag. Got dark quick now that summer was getting ready to go, so they couldn't make out who. Ol' Nip, even with his old eyes, he knew. Must have smelled ahead. Barked a how do.

Toby was off those church steps faster than Early had seen him move in all the last few days. Chub also ran up, kinda breathless, like maybe she'd run a lot to get there.

"Hey, Early," she said, looking at Toby.

Chub knelt and gave Ol' Nip a biscuit. First she had to crumble it, his teeth mostly being gone. She said she asked her aunt to get some biscuits so she could give them to Mikki's dog, but she really meant them for Ol' Nip.

"Thought you weren't allowed here anymore?"

"They think I'm at Leeza's house."

"That girl at school? You friends now?"

Chub spit, the kind that sealed an oath.

"No. I hate her. She punched me in the stomach so hard I almost cried, but I didn't. Says I'm a tar baby and when the sisters don't hear, she makes her friends call me that."

"So how come you go to her house?"

"I don't. She telephones me all the time, then hangs up so nobody knows it's her. But I do. So tonight when she called, I answered loud for my mom and Aunt Joy to hear: 'Oh yes, Leeza, I'd love to come over and study.' Should've heard her on the other end. 'I never asked you to come over you ugly little troll.' But I just said see ya. Then some man from my aunt's work came and picked her up.

I hope it's a date and they get married and she moves out. That's why I'm here and no one knows. As if anyone cares."

Toby said they were inside the church.

"My aunt's here?"

"Came with some man."

"Whatcha got in the bag?"

"Something real cool, Toby, for me and you."

Early wanted to see too, but Toby said he had to be the lookout by the church door and let them know if anyone was coming. Then Chub and Toby went by the corner of the building where Early could still hear them, and give the signal. Ol' Nip took his time getting up the stairs to where Early was, then crawled into his lap. When Early leaned back against the church door to get a better look at the night coming, it opened a bit.

We don't have hundreds of thousands of dollars to bring water and sewage pipes through the rocks down here.

Sounded like a lot of money. How many Cherry Blossoms could that get? Early thought about asking Toby—he'd know—but he was on duty and Chub was talking.

"It's a walkie-talkie. One for you. One for me. They used to be my brother's, but he doesn't want them any more. So I took 'em."

A flock of ducks passed overhead. You could hear the air when it got pushed out from under their wings. They settled down on the harbour where the moon was shining and sounded like they were having a good laugh.

Chub was showing how the walkie-talkie worked. It was making static noises, like when the TV went all snowy.

"Maybe the batteries are no good."

"Got batteries?"

"Yeah, in back. See?"

"Hey, what happened on your arm?"

"Oh nothing, just got cut, that's all."

"Dog next door get you?"

"Yeah, I guess."

Ol' Nip was asleep. Only sounds coming out of him were soft popping farts. Those biscuits hadn't gone down too good.

I've been listening to you people now, talking about all this moving business and I'd like to say something.

Sit down, Aada.

No I won't sit down, Aubrey Daye. I'm going to speak my mind, if you won't. My name is Mrs. Aada Dupuis. Lived in my house my whole life, on a piece of land my daddy got from his daddy. My grandfather was William Brown and he got that land in 1848, legal and proper. When my daddy got married, he got a piece. And when my first husband come around, Jesse English, I got a piece of that. Jess and me didn't have much time together, buried two boys after they got caught running across the train tracks back there, and my last one, Ralph, he's the deacon in this church and I am very proud of him. After Jess goes I got another husband. He's gone now too, but I still got that house over by the pond with all the memories. Now, how many of you folks sitting up there can say you live on land your grandfather owned?

Honking came really soft at first, from far away.

Chub was saying roger over and out into her walkie-talkie.

I'm not some old fool with bad eyes. I can see what's wrong down here just like you city people can. Places falling down, wells bad in the summer, outdoor toilets, and I know squatters are doing things against the law, not mindful to the rest of us.

Early heard him and D Jay called squatters lots of times.

But it wasn't always like folks gave up down here. Let me tell you something, I remember after the first war, Africville got pretty wild in those days. Got so I didn't think it was fit to raise children. My Jess, he knew otherwise. Him and a few others got up to city hall and said we pay taxes down there in Africville so we need the police, we need good water so our kids don't get sick. I can tell you, nothing happened. After the next war, same thing. That time, even got the city to put aside money for sewers, so you might want to check in that city hall of yours because I think that money's sitting around in someone's desk. Sure didn't get spent down here.

Some folks chuckled inside.

The honking noise was getting louder.

"You hear that?" said Toby.

"Yeah, geese. Must be going to Florida. That's where Derek says they go."

All we ever wanted, Mrs Aada was saying, *was what*

other folks already got. Why all the meetings? Do we stay, do we go? Just give us what we deserve so maybe the young ones will want to stay here and not go first chance they get. Stay here and try to get things better. No point you people sitting up there all holier than thou, thinking you talk for Africville. I'm Africville. Aubrey Daye here is Africville. I don't even know you people. And you sure don't talk for me.

Aubrey kept whispering for Mrs. Aada to be quiet and to sit down.

And where are we supposed to go? Big fancy developments in the city? Tell me, I'm going to be able to take Mrs. Trilby with me? She's my cow, sir. Am I going to be able to look out my kitchen window and see the Bedford Basin? What about this church? I've been part of this church my whole life. Baptized in it. Married in it. I don't want a new one, somewhere I've never been. And who's going to take care of the ones like Blind Emmett when he's out of milk or needs help getting out of bed when his arthritis gets him all knotted up? Can you answer me that?

Early figured this time of year was the best. Warm days, but you didn't notice the smell from the dump so much. Quiet nights, like tonight. Swore if he tried, he could hear every single voice in the big town talking, not mumble jumble together, but each one alone, what they got to say, and why.

Out there on the harbour, a ship piled with barrels was going slow across the white moon path, not a peep out of her. Early wondered what she was carrying.

"So if you have one and I have one, then we can talk to each other every night before we go to sleep. No one'll know."

"Neat," said Toby.

I'm seventy years old. I figure I can do without a flush toilet for the rest of my days. What I can't do without are the sunflowers in my backyard or hear my dead kids wanting to go swimming in the pond because they're still with me, yes they are, in that house, my house, not something the city owns. You talk about us moving as being better. Integration being better. Better for who? You think I want to live in some city project by white folks who don't want to live by me? So what you're really saying is, you're going to give us a spoonful of sugar to take our homes from us whether we want it or not.

Ol' Nip looked up sleepily as the geese passed overhead. Early whispered to Chub and Toby if they thought the birds might stop and get rested, but they didn't say.

"So now I can help you with your homework, like we planned."

"How long you going to that new school?"

"Dad said he got extra money 'cause of something that happened to his ears in the navy that he didn't even know was wrong, but if you can screw it out of the government, why not? That's what he says pays for my school."

"You think Grandpa could get money?"

"Naw. I asked my dad, said what about my friend Toby's grandpa, he was in the war too. He said I was silly thinking a Negro fought in the war for our Queen."

"He did. And it was the King."

"I know that, Toby, I'm just saying."

Someone inside said a Doctor Rose was visiting in November. He knew about urban renewal and was a big shot in Toronto. Nothing after that, except singing from a house up the road. The door to the church must have closed and Toby and Chub weren't saying much either.

Early remembered D Jay saying his boy got holes in his brain on account of his mother drinking lots when he was in her belly. D Jay used to make him drink lots of that homemade stuff of Knowl's. Said it was better than a tit for a baby, 'cause it stopped him crying. Sometimes he'd make Early down a whole bottle when he got older, laughing when he couldn't stand up. Must be so, about the holes then. Early sure didn't hold on to things. But Early got to thinking, sitting on those stairs, and it came to him. So quiet out, he could hear the crickets. Not long now before they got frozen silent. Waves from the ship that passed were starting to splash splash splash against the beach. He watched Toby and Chub sitting on the grass talking, and he knew for sure this one thing and that he wouldn't forget: Toby was sure glad to have a friend like Chub.

TOBY WAS AFRAID HIS BIRTHDAY WAS GOING TO get lost that year.

"How come?"

"It's not far, Early, and Mrs. Aada hasn't asked me about my cake. She always makes me a cake, and this year I want a penny cake."

"Huh?"

"You know, she puts pennies in it when it's cooking so you find them when you eat it."

"Can you keep 'em? Enough for Cherry Blossoms?"

"Sure, I guess. And you know, Penny is Chub's other name, so she'll have to come to my party. If I have one. She'll just have to."

Toby was shaking the walkie-talkie. Even though he pressed the button and kept saying roger roger, nothing but static came out of it. That's all it had done since Chub gave it to him.

"Every time I go over there, she's just staring out her window. And guess what, this morning, she had a cigarette."

"Never saw Mrs. Aada have a smoke."

"I know."

After Early finished milking Mrs. Trilby, he brought the milk into Mrs. Aada's store, like always.

"Oh, Early. What am I going to do with that?"

Milk? Cream? Butter?

"I mean poor Mrs. Trilby. What'll happen to her?"

"I watch out for her, you know that."

Mrs. Aada smiled. Funny though, she didn't look one bit happy.

"You have to start watching out for yourself."

Maybe Mrs. Aada needed to get busy like Aubrey. Right after the meeting in the church he said to Early, Early, we got to get going on finishing Jubilee Hall for Miss Portia. Any day now, all things being equal, you'll see.

The stage needed fixing, and more seats. Walls to be painted and Aubrey wanted to run a wire from Mrs. Aada's house so there'd be electric lights inside and not those lanterns hanging on the beams. Sometimes Aubrey'd be so tired at the end of the day with all the to-ing and fro-ing, he'd fall asleep sitting up at his kitchen table without eating.

Maybe that Dr. Rose coming to check things out would give something to Mrs. Aada and Aubrey to make them feel better.

"Maybe so, Early," said Toby. "Maybe so."

Toby's birthday didn't get forgotten. Mrs. Aada made dinner and they wore paper crowns that came out of crackers. She baked Toby a Boston cream pie, and that was not a pie at all, but a real cake. It had cream in the middle and chocolate frosting, but no pennies. Thank you very much, but Toby gave his piece to Early. That was because Chub didn't come down for his party. Deborah didn't come by either with any money, so all Aubrey could give Toby were new batteries for the walkie-talkie. Maybe it would work better. But Early had two big pieces of cake that he shared with Ol' Nip.

"I thought for sure we'd hear from Miss Portia, it being the boy's special day," said Aubrey. "Maybe I should go over to Ruby's and ask, just in case a letter came in late."

He could do that without Mrs. Aada. She wasn't joining in that tomfoolery as she had washing up to do.

"Toby, get your coat if you're coming with me."

He came back with one for him and one for Early.

"Early, is that all you got to wear for a coat?"

"Yes."

"You'll freeze this winter. We gotta get you something that fits right."

Aubrey and Ol' Nip were taking their sweet old time so Early and Toby got ahead on the road.

"You think she forgot?" Toby was looking up the hill at those lights. He had it all figured which ones were Chub's. "Oh, it doesn't matter."

Early felt bad for Toby, it being his day and all. He didn't know when his birthday was. D Jay never said except it was on a day he wanted to forget. So Toby gave Early a birthday on the same day as the baby Jesus because there was lots going on that day and no one would mind one more birthday snuck in. Mrs. Aada would make a cake for sure. Wonder if he'd get one with pennies like Toby wanted.

"You wanna piggyback?"

"Naw."

They waited on the road for Aubrey to come out of Miss Ruby's with Ol' Nip. No letter.

"Any day now, boys. That's what she said."

The walk back was quiet. Early started to whistle until Toby poked him in the ribs.

"Who's that? I expect she's for you, son."

Chub was sitting on the porch waiting. That girl, always showed up when Toby needed it most.

"I thought you forgot."

Early told her that Mrs. Aada made a pie that wasn't a pie and he had double helpings.

"How many did you have?"

"I wasn't hungry," said Toby.

"Good, because I have a surprise for you."

"Yeah?"

Ol' Nip let out a little bark. He and Aubrey had enough surprises for one day and they were going to bed.

"What's the surprise?"

"C'mon over to my house. You too, Early."

"Really?"

"Yeah. My dad's at the hospital with Mom."

"She okay?"

"Oh, sure. She got some new medicine that made her dizzy, so they're just checking. Derek was supposed to stay at home with me, but Eddie called him for a sleepover." Chub rolled her eyes. "Right next door. So I said I'd call my friend Leeza and go stay with her, you know, like I did before. And my aunt's working late. They'll be gone for hours, so c'mon. Early, you'd better take 'im on your back. It'll be faster."

They ran around the turn, got over the first tracks, and started climbing the hill. When they pushed through the bushes around the higher tracks and came out in behind Chub's house, she had them wait while she went inside to turn on lights. A couple minutes later, there she was at the door, waving.

Toby stopped on the porch.

"It's all right, you can come in."

He was looking inside.

"There's carpet."

Wall-to-wall and there was also a sofa with big orange and yellow flowers and a wooden cabinet full of china. Chub said the plates were called Lavender Rose and her grandmother gave them money to buy the cabinet. In the corner was an ashtray on a stand all by itself, made of marble and glass, and a wall clock that looked like the sun with rays. Everything was so grand.

"Here, Toby, try this chair."

It was green leather and when he leaned back the bottom popped open for his feet to rest on.

"That used to be my grandfather's La-Z-Boy. We got it after he died in it listening to a hockey game. C'mon in the kitchen."

Chub made them sit around a grey table with squiggly black and white patterns. She said she and her brother had a game to find the ones that looked like s's.

"I'm going to bake you a birthday cake."

A penny cake like Toby wanted but Mrs. Aada didn't bake?

"Okay."

"You know how?"

"Easy. I helped my mom lots, when she could still do it. Did one all by myself too. Want something to drink?"

When she opened the refrigerator for the milk, Toby gave Early a nudge.

"See that?"

Early sure did. No one went hungry in this house.

Chub was looking through the cupboard for a cake mix.

"It's really simple. You just add water and eggs and beat it, then put it in the oven. Then see? This canned frosting goes on top."

Early wanted to know if it was chocolate because that was his favourite.

Toby couldn't drink his milk. He was shaking.

"You okay?"

He nodded.

Chub started mixing the cake together, adding a cup of water, cracking an egg, then she poured the batter into a square pan, filling it right to the top.

"Don't worry about the lumps. They'll go away." She slid the cake into the oven. "Oops, forgot to turn it on. I'll turn it up high. C'mon, let's go upstairs."

That was where the bedrooms were. One big one for her folks, two others, one for her, one for her brother. At the top of the stairs was a white wooden table with a lamp made out of copper.

"Hey Toby, it's got a dog on it."

"Early, that's a bear."

"Look what my brother got me. He wrote away and asked and they sent me this picture with all the autographs on it. It's the Forest Rangers. That's Ranger Keeley and Sergeant Scott and that's Joe Two Rivers. There's Chub Stanley. He's my favourite. And that's Pete, Mike, Timmy, and Kathy. They're junior rangers. See, everyone signed it. Neat, huh?"

Toby agreed.

The room had a bed and a desk beside the closet door. Also a dresser covered with dolls.

"Oh, those. I get one every Christmas. They're supposed to be my collection, but I hate them. It's like those airplane models my dad puts together for Derek. Hangs them from his ceiling."

Early wanted to know what the rope ladder coiled underneath the sill was for.

"Fires."

Chub's mother was terrified of them, so Chub could throw the ladder out her window if she had to get down fast.

"It's pretty good for getting out of the house and no one seeing you."

Empty peanut butter jars lined the sill, with holes punched in the lids. Inside each one, a snail munched its way through a lettuce leaf.

"Aunt Joy told me to get rid of them, so now I have six. Wanna see where you live?"

Mostly what they saw were lights, night coming, but Toby knew which ones belonged to Mrs. Jensen's house with the crooked chimney, Blind Emmett's with the overturned bathtub out back he grew dahlias in, Mr. Sumlar's with the TV antenna, and Old Irene's with the tarpaper roof.

"And there's Big Town, Early, where we live."

Chub and Toby were squished together in the window having a look.

"You know what? In the day, I know when it's you and Early down there on the tracks."

"Wish I could see it from here all the time."

"Cake sure smells good, Chub," said Early.

First, Toby made Early come over to the window and have a look. Then they went back downstairs to the kitchen, which was a good thing because when they got there, they heard hissing inside the oven.

Chub uh-oh-ed when she opened the door. The rising cake had spilled over the side and was dripping onto the bottom of the stove.

"That's okay, I can fix it."

Chub got the spoon and bowl she'd mixed the batter in from over by the sink.

"Here, Toby, hold this."

She scooped some of the uncooked cake from the centre of the pan.

"There. Oops, almost forgot the pennies."

She had to run upstairs for those and when she returned, she sprinkled them into the half-cooked cake. Toby and Early thought that was neat.

When Toby and Early were back around the table and looking for s's, Chub got some rose-decorated plates from the china cabinet in the living room.

"We only use these for Christmas and special occasions."

"Looks like the flowers behind Miss Ruby's house."

"Yeah, Toby. Looks like 'em for sure."

Chub handed Early and Toby each a silver fork. She said they weren't stainless steel, but the real McCoy, silver plate, because her Grandma Deforest bought things at Eaton's. The cake done, Chub put it on the counter to cool.

"Sorry about that, Toby." She meant how it looked, a hole in the centre and where the batter had spilled over, burnt black. "It'll look better when it's got icing."

"Can Early lick the spoon when you're finished?"

Good old Toby. It was his birthday and here was Early getting the best part.

One more thing to do. Chub found a box of birthday candles in the kitchen junk drawer.

"There, ten."

She made Early sing "Happy Birthday" to Toby with her, but it wasn't easy going, him licking that spoon at the same time.

"I almost forgot."

Chub flicked off the kitchen lights. Around the table they could only see each other in shadow, lit by candles.

"Now you look just like me and Early, Toby, like you want. Blow out the candles."

He wanted them to last, but the wax melted quickly.

The light back on, Chub cut squares around the wax blobs in the middle, more to the side. One piece for Toby, one for her, and a big one for Early. The cake was kind of wet, like maybe not cooked enough, but Toby didn't mind because he was first to pull a coin out of his mouth. They were having such a good time, no one heard the front door close and footsteps in the hall.

"Penny, what the hell's going on in here? And what's burning?"

The woman opened the oven door.

"You make this mess?"

The three faces around the table stared back. Early thought the woman looked just as pinched as the last time he saw her, going into the church.

"Sorry, Aunt Joy. I just wanted to do a surprise for my friend Toby."

"I can see that. Sweetie, you scared the hell out of me. Where is everyone?"

Chub told her.

Toby and Early figured the woman was going to phone the police. Chub looked like she was between being mad and being scared. Aunt Joy—Early thought he was liking her after that scowl left her face—opened the window to air out the burnt smell.

"It was for Toby's birthday," said Chub.

Aunt Joy was taking a deep breath. And another. Then she rubbed her forehead.

"Penny, your friends better go now so we can clean up before your mom and dad get home."

"You gonna tell?"

"We'll talk about that later, but if we don't clean up, they're going to know as soon as they walk in."

"Okay, but I have to get something first."

Chub went downstairs to the basement and came back with a corduroy coat.

"Here, Early. I was going to give you this."

"For me?"

"My brother put it in the bag for the Salvation Army. He says it makes him look fat. There's a tear on the elbow, but maybe Mrs. Aada can fix it so you can't see."

Early pulled on the coat.

"Fits you better than that old thing you got. And warmer."

"Thank you, Chub."

"Yeah, thanks."

Then Aunt Joy showed the boys the door.

THE NEW BATTERIES AUBREY GAVE TOBY FOR HIS
walkie-talkie worked, but only if Toby and Early didn't go
past the bottom of the hill near Chub's place, and voices
still got scratched up.

"You get in trouble?"

"I can't hear. Talk louder."

"I said, you get in trouble?"

"You have to say 'over' when you're finished talking,
like they do on *The Forest Rangers*."

"You get in trouble? Over."

"Yeah. My folks got back from the hospital before me
and Aunt Joy cleaned up. Mom had to lie down with a
couple of Aspirins. Derek thought I was going to get the
strap for sure. Over."

"Did you? I mean, over."

"No. Dad still had his belt on. No way out of it if the
belt's off. But he sure yelled. Mikki next door heard. He
wanted to know if I was crazy letting you guys in the
house. Said I might have got beaten up or robbed or got

some kinda disease, or worse. I told him no way would you do that to me and boy, was he red in the face. Over."

Toby and Early wondered if she was afraid, but Chub said she didn't care about her dad or getting that belt, or if he was going to be up all night drinking milk of magnesia to settle his stomach because he felt bad about strapping her.

"He goes, you look at me, young lady, when I'm talking to you. But I didn't. I looked at that mole on his neck, thinking it might start to talk it was getting so big, just getting madder and madder, letting stuff go 'round in my head. That's when I said, 'Don't tell me not to do things I'm not supposed to. I saw you kissing Aunt Joy at that card game.' Over."

"What'd he say? Over."

"Friends sometimes kiss. Hello. Good-bye. Dad said Aunt Joy was going through hard times, and he was lonely even though Mom hadn't gone anywhere and I shouldn't be making things up about it, especially to Mom. Over."

"Guess you can't come out for a while. Over."

"No. But Derek was some mad when he came into my room to see my strap marks. He said I got off easy 'cause I'm a girl. Over."

Early wanted a try, but the batteries gave up right about then.

*⬿

Snow came the first week of November. Not much, but wet and heavy. Some of the trees snapped their branches on top of the power lines, knocking out the electricity. That meant days of being cold inside and cooking over an open flame. The power company always came last to Africville.

Aubrey said November was his thinking month. Maybe it was because the muddy road got full of holes, more so than usual, all that freezing and thawing starting. Meant you didn't get around much. Leaves were pretty well gone, having taken summer and the sunflowers with them. Grey days, grey days, sure made yards heaped with rusting fridges and broken cars, piles of wood, fencing all crooked look like the dump was moulting.

Toby said it was because of Remembrance Day, the one day of the year when Aubrey got that old uniform of his out of the cedar chest, pressed it, and hung it from a hook in his room. He usually made it to the parade square in front of city hall, but not this year, not with the weather and his wooden leg and no money for the bus.

Chub showed up at the door eating snow. She got half the day off from school to go to the cenotaph. No one at her house was going. She said her Aunt Joy was working because it would be quiet in the office and she could get loads of typing done without people going, Joy, we need this, Joy, type that right away, Joy, get me a coffee. Everyone else was sleeping in.

"Hello, Chub. The boys are at the kitchen table."

She'd never seen Aubrey in a uniform smelling of moth balls. Ol' Nip didn't care for it either. That's why he was sitting on the side of his bum way over in the doorway to the shadowy living room, there being no sun outside.

"No school today, honey?" Mrs. Aada was by the sink, heating milk over a camp stove.

"We're supposed to be remembering."

"That's what we're doing," Early said.

Toby pulled out a chair for Chub.

"You were in the war, huh, Mr. Daye?"

"The first big one."

"My dad was in one too. He worked at the navy. How come you're dressed in that?"

"Because, Chub, today's the day for thinking about some of the fellows I went over there with, and who didn't come back. Have a drink to their memory."

"We're helping," said Toby.

"Don't you be serving them no drink, Aubrey Daye. Those kids are having hot chocolate as soon as this milk is ready."

Ol' Nip let out a hello-I'm-here bark. Chub gave a scratch behind his ear.

"Mrs. Trilby okay with the snow?"

"She was hollering about it this morning, but there's not much she can do about it."

"She needs a house."

Mrs. Aada put down three mugs of hot chocolate.

Aubrey got a bottle from the cupboard over the sink, poured some into a glass, then the bottle went back.

"Everybody ready?"

They all sipped and remained quiet. No one made hot chocolate like Mrs. Aada. Real thick, and she put in those miniature marshmallows that melt creamy on the top.

"Mr. Daye, what was it like?"

"Don't you get started telling those kids war stories," said Mrs. Aada.

"No, no, they should hear. Once a year won't hurt for them to know these things."

"How old were you?"

"A bit younger than Early. I was sixteen, Chub, when the Great War broke out. 1914. I wanted to sign up right away, but my folks said I was too young and my ma didn't want me going at all."

"Army didn't take coloured folks."

"Well, missus, things were different then. My two best friends, Chester Lupee and Jimmy Fyles—Chester, he was from here, Jimmy come down from Jacob Street—well, we got so worked up about the war, hearing about France, figured it'd all be over before we got a chance to fight. Even thought we'd get down to the States, sign up there. But we didn't have a pot to piss in."

Mrs. Aada had something to say about that.

"So how'd you get over?" asked Chub.

"About two years into the war, the government made a company only for coloured men."

Missus made that noise she does. Sort of like air getting brushed out of her nose with a broom.

"Only because too many white boys were getting killed. You want some more chocolate, Early?"

"Yes."

"Yes, what?"

"Yes, please."

"Don't matter what the reason was. Me and Chester and Jimmy were first in line down at the recruiting office, getting our uniforms, this very one I'm wearing today. Sent us up to Pictou for training. Now we all thought we'd be getting overseas real quick. Specially Chester. Had a thing for the ladies, Chester did, and he was in a real hurry to find out about those French gals."

"For heaven's sake, Aubrey."

"That's all I'm saying about that. Now about the war, turns out we had to wait awhile. After they marched us around up in Pictou, even taught me how to shoot a rifle, they sent us to Truro. Coloured boys from all over Canada met up there. Made some real good friends."

"You still know 'em, Grandpa?"

Funny look came over Aubrey right then. He didn't talk much about the war at other times, and he seemed to be right pleased about sharing his story for Chub. Still, parts of it didn't come easy, like this one.

"You know, Toby, I guess I'm the last. Now let's see, yeah, we finally got the order to go. Spring of 1917. Brought us down to the pier in Halifax and put us on the *Southland*, going to England. Saw my folks there before I went; all worried they was about me going. Turns out, it was the last I saw of my pa. Come Christmas, he was dead right in the living room there, from the explosion in the harbour."

Aubrey got up from the table and went into his room. When he came out, he had a piece of a rusted metal bar in his hand.

"A piece of railing from the *Mont Blanc*. Right through him, standing in front of the window over there watering a geranium."

"Fine thing, showing that to these kids."

"Why? It's a piece of history. That explosion happened here in Africville too, not that folks remember."

Chub wanted Aubrey to get to the good part, like when he lost his leg.

"I'm getting to that. Now it took us more than a week to get to England. Sure do talk funny there, but you know, not so mindful of coloureds like here. Oh, and beer's good too. Poor Jimmy, puked the whole way over. Had to sleep on deck in the rain. But he was okay once we got him on dry land. After a couple of weeks, we got sent to France, a place called Péronne."

"We're studying the French Revolution in school. I'd love to see Paris. That's where they chop off heads."

"What I saw was mostly bombed-out villages. Chester, he did all right. Got himself a real nice lady friend, Italian girl. Thought he might stay on after the war was over and get married. Jimmy, he got real lonesome for home. Kept talking about building his own place down here in Africville, getting his folks out of that Jacob Street flat. Got me thinking too, wishing for summer nights and fishing."

"Did he come back?"

There was that look again.

"Can't say that he did. One night, the three of us were outside our tent having a smoke. Damnedest thing. There was Chester in the middle lighting a match. Lights it for me, then for Jimmy. When he lights his own smoke, that's when it hit. All I remember now is a flash. Killed them both, took out my leg. Patched me up, doctor said it served me right having three on a match, gave me the news my old man was dead and most of Halifax gone, and sent me home. Left Chester and Jimmy buried over there. Felt bad about doing that to Jimmy, but I know Chester would've been all right with staying."

Ol' Nip flipped over and sighed.

"That's enough remembering for today," Mrs. Aada said, getting up so no one could see her wipe her eyes. "You'll have these kids afraid to go to sleep."

"Not me. I want to go to a war," said Chub. "Shoot a gun. Get to see the world."

"There, Aubrey, look what you've done. Young lady, where's that loose talk coming from? Girls don't belong in the army and Lord knows, men don't either."

"She's right. Only good thing about war, you know who your enemy is."

That night loud D Jay-like talk woke Early up, something about papers getting lost. Toby was bent in against the wall hearing nothing, so Early got up and started pulling all his clothes together in case his pops wanted him to leave right away. He didn't forget that new coat from Chub. When he got to the bedroom door and had a whiff of perfume, that's when he realized, hey. It wasn't D Jay. It was Toby's mom having a go at Aubrey.

"C'mon, Dad, you're lying to me. You must know where it is."

"Somewhere, I'm sure. Don't know where your mother left those things."

"How could you not know where the deed is?"

"It's in my papers."

"Where? Damn it."

"I don't know why you need it right now. It's late."

"Christ, it's all over the news, Dad, the city is going to toss you out of here. Unless you've got a deed, you'll get peanuts."

"No, no, no, they've said that before and nothing ever happens."

Sounded to Early like stuff was getting thrown around out there in the living room.

"When Miss Portia comes here to sing, you'll see. Africville'll be on the map."

"It's on the map now, right next to the city dump."

"Deborah, you'll wake the boys."

"Then find me the fucking deed. I'm not going to be cheated out of what's mine."

"In the morning, I'm too tired now. Why don't you sit and let me make you a cup of tea? Since you're visiting, maybe you could give me some money to help out. I'm behind on the electricity. Feels like it'll be a cold winter."

"You think I got money? Why do you think I'm here

trying to find that bloody piece of paper? I owe people, Dad."

"Who? That Knowl? Always said he was bad news, getting you hooked on that stuff."

"Christ, not that again."

"Honey, this house is all I got to take care of me and Toby. And now with Early staying here—"

"No one asked you."

"It's just till his father gets back."

"D Jay Okander is halfway to hell. Everyone but you knows that. He's probably thousands of miles away from here, and he sure as hell don't give a damn about his idiot kid."

"Don't say that. He's Toby's friend."

"Yeah? If the city takes this place from you, you got bigger problems without worrying about where Early's going to end up."

It quieted down after that.

Early had a scratch. Why would they be worried about where he was going? He knew, and crawled back into bed on the floor beside Toby.

TOBY WAS MILKING MRS. TRILBY, HIS HEAD UP, having a look for something every now and then. Early was shovelling her turds. One cow sure made a lot, but Mrs. Aada said what do you expect? That cow just eats and shits all day and no, Early can't fill the wheelbarrow and take it down to the pond and let it go. She wanted the shit to go to the dump and that was too far for Toby. So Toby did the milking, Early shovelled.

"You been to a doctor, Toby?"

"Grandpa says he and Mrs. Aada the only doctors I need."

"Then how come we gotta clean up around here for that doctor of Mrs. Aada's?"

"It's not that kinda doctor, Early. Not one that fixes people. This one knows a lot of things, that's why they call him a doctor."

"So, what does he know?"

"Mrs. Aada says Dr. Rose is the best one in the country to fix things, like the problem with Africville."

"What problem?"

Mrs. Aada had her head out the window saying cows don't milk themselves.

"And Toby, if you're finished, get that bucket in here and Early, off to the dump with you. Sure wish there was time to get a coat o'paint on your place, Toby, but it's the wrong time of year for that. Your grandfather should have minded me in the spring. Get in here and let me have a look at that skin rash of yours."

Early winked at Toby about that and helped him carry the bucket of milk into the kitchen. Then it was back to getting the full wheelbarrow to the dump. It was not going to be easy. Aubrey said it was the Indian summer that melted the snow filling the potholes with puddles. No telling how deep they were until you were stuck in them and your feet were wet. Then, past the church, Early met up with Tom and Charlie.

"Whatcha got there, Early?"

"Takin' Mrs. Trilby's shit to the dump."

"'Taking Mrs. Trilby's shit to the dump.'"

He didn't know why Charlie repeated that, in a high funny voice.

"Good job for you, lame brain, haulin' crap."

"Can't do that with you standin' in front of me."

"'Can't do that with you standing in front of me.'"

There Charlie went again, laughing.

"Where's your little puppy?"

"Got no puppy."

"Toby Daye. Woof. Woof."

Tom said, "Ah c'mon, he doesn't get it. Stupid arse."

"You know, you'd better watch out. If me and Tom get hungry, that cow of yours could end up getting eaten."

"Don't you touch Mrs. Trilby."

Charlie was laughing. "Look at 'im, crying over a cow. C'mon, let's go."

But not before he kicked over the wheelbarrow.

Early got the wheelbarrow upright. The old turds were easy to get back in, they were hard, but the new ones were like mud. Then it was on his way to finish what he'd started.

"You stink." Chub plugged her nose when she came along, skipping and jumping over puddles. "What's that all over you?"

"Mrs. Trilby's shit."

"Yech."

She was pretty good now at making the shortcut down the hill from her place.

"I'm supposed to be at a movie with Derek, but he wants to go see *Cleopatra* again, says it's his favourite movie and they won't let me in 'cause I'm too young."

"Who's that?"

"Cleopatra? She was the queen of Egypt a long time ago. Derek's in love with her."

"The queen?"

"No, Elizabeth Taylor. She's pretending to be a queen. Derek's got lots of pictures of her in a scrapbook."

"Oh." Aubrey had one of those for Miss Portia.

"So I said to my brother, fine, go see your stupid movie a hundred zillion times, but give me my money and I'll do something else."

Early found it much easier going back with the wheelbarrow empty.

"Where's Toby?"

"Mrs. Aada's lookin' at his rash."

"You didn't say anything about that, did you, Early?"

"No."

"Good."

Way up at the end of the road where it went over the train tracks, Early saw a police car. Didn't see them very much. Sometimes they came to D Jay's when he had a card game on and the noise was out of hand. Sounds could travel at night and bother folks up where Chub lived. But most times, cops didn't come to Africville.

Aubrey opened his door to say hello as Chub and Early turned off the main road and onto his lane. Ol' Nip, he made it out too, took one look at Chub and made that hello bark of his, before waddling his way over. Must have been sleeping. His back legs were kinda stiff. He didn't see so well anymore, and he sure never saw the police car coming down the road, turning onto the lane and swerving to miss him. The policeman beside the driver had his window open. Stuck his gun out and fired. Ol' Nip's back legs went down, but he kept trying to get to Chub, so the policeman fired again.

"You okay, young lady?" he said, stepping out of the car.

Chub stared at him. Mrs. Aada and Toby ran out of her house. Missus, she let out an oh, no. Early didn't think she cared much for the dog. That was more than Aubrey or Toby could do. Sounded like Chub was starting to choke.

The other policeman got out of the car, put on his hat and wanted to know who owned the vicious dog.

"He's mine," said Aubrey. "Had him since he was a pup."

"Got reports of dogs roaming wild down here, barking all night. If you people took care of your animals, you wouldn't let them loose. That girl could have been mauled. You're lucky, kid."

On the way back into their car, the policeman who'd done the shooting sniffed. You smell that? Then they drove on past the church towards the dump, going real slow on account of the holes in the road.

Aubrey sat, right there. Not easy for him to do with that leg of his, ground being cold. He took Ol' Nip in his lap and put his hand on the dog's head. Mrs. Aada looked down the road after the police car like maybe she lost something or didn't know where she was. Early got the shovel he'd used to clean up after Mrs. Trilby.

"Where you going?"

Out behind Jubilee Hall. Early figured Aubrey'd want to put Ol' Nip there. The top few inches of ground were cold and hard to break through, but after he did, he dug a right nice square, good and deep, like he did for his girls. When he came back to the road, everyone except Aubrey looked at him. Chub wiped her eyes with her mitten and Toby said not now.

"No, the boy's right, son. You take him, Early."

So he did, and carefully buried the dog while Mrs. Trilby watched. Chub was gone when he finished. Mrs. Aada took Aubrey inside by the arm like he got old real fast and couldn't do it by himself. She was going back and forth in front of the kitchen window, so Mrs. Aada must have sat him down at his table and was making him tea.

A few days later, Miss Ruby told Aubrey, if you blinked, you missed it.

She was talking about that Dr. Rose coming from Toronto to write a report for the city about what to do with Africville. He didn't need more than a few hours seeing, or having to talk to anyone, to know how things should be.

And no, Aubrey, no letter from Miss White.

EARLY GOT UP QUIETLY SO AS NOT TO WAKE TOBY, and pulled the wet sheet off his mattress. Then he stepped out of his underwear. Aubrey kept a towel for him on the shelf beside Toby's bed so Early could dry off, get into his pants, and wash his things out in the kitchen sink.

The Christmas tree lights were still on. Aubrey waited all year for the holidays and as it was, they hurried by too fast. He wanted to see those bright colours for as long as he could even if there was the matter of an electric bill.

Not a bad-looking tree, coming from where it did. Toby wanted to get one from the lots up on Gottingen Street, one grown special for Christmas and that touched the ceiling and was so thick you couldn't see the trunk. Aubrey said there were just as many good trees behind D Jay's place, and they were free for the cutting. Got a nice tall one, and on the table, it almost touched the roof.

No one was up yet, except maybe Mrs. Trilby. Early didn't know when she slept or even if cows slept at all. Day wasn't night anymore. Instead, it was kind of a grey because of all the new snow making it white outside, making it not so dark inside, making it easy to see that present wrapped for Chub under the tree.

Boy, was she going to be surprised. It was from Toby, but Early and Aubrey and even Mrs. Aada helped. At first, Toby didn't know what to do about getting Chub a gift. Kept asking what she'd like, had to be special, no, had to be perfect. Like Aubrey said, that's a tough order to fill, son. First everyone thought, something for her bike, but Toby knew she wouldn't be keen. Young ladies should have barrettes for their hair. Mrs. Aada said that was her two cents. Even Early knew Chub wouldn't go for that. Aubrey had a good idea. How about a tomahawk because she wanted to be a Fire Ranger—Grandpa, that's a Forest Ranger—but they didn't know any Indians.

Best thing you could give Chub was Africville. Being there with them was all she wanted. Didn't she say so, lots?

Aubrey and Toby and Mrs. Aada said, Early's right. Early figured they were having a laugh on him. Can't give Chub a whole town. Yes you could. Aubrey had seen it done before when he used to go into the city on a tram. Called them snow globes. Saw it in a Mills Brothers department store window, all made up for Christmas with mechanical elves that waved you inside to visit Santa. Miniature towns in glass balls full of water and when you shook them, it snowed. Perfect. They'd make one for Chub, but it'd be Africville getting snowed on. Covered in snow is when Africville looked best.

With Mrs. Aada's and Aubrey's fingers too old to do up-close work and Toby feeling poorly—flu said his grandpa—Early made all the houses, even the church and Jubilee Hall. Only he didn't make that shed out back of D Jay's. He didn't want Chub thinking about that. Then he made people so Chub would know that it was him and Toby and his grandpa and Mrs. Aada. That wasn't all. Even got Ol' Nip, Mrs. Trilby, and the chickens. Thanks, Early, said Toby, that's everyone.

Early finished washing his bedsheet in the sink hoping Chub'd make a visit. Maybe she could forget about her mom being sick and her aunt moving in if she did. Toby couldn't wait to give her the snow globe and since Christmas Day got to be Early's birthday, then Chub coming would be like a present for him too.

Outside, it looked like Africville got a good dusting. That's what Aubrey said about any snowfall although it looked to Early that a lot more than dust came over night. The drifts were up to his knees on the way to the clothesline out back to hang his sheet. Mrs. Trilby watched him, not looking too happy about having been out all night. Snow blown thick and hanging round off the roof looked like that cap Aubrey kept on a nail by the door, road so smoothed over you didn't even know where it ran. The place'd be quiet now. If the road didn't get plowed, the cars couldn't get through. Nothing could.

Except for Mrs. Aada.

What was she doing out there at this time of day? She couldn't be washing sheets and underwear like Early. She was standing in the snow, coat on over her nightgown, looking at the silvery blue harbour. Must have eyes in the back of her head because Mrs. Aada didn't look to see Early, she just starting talking.

"He bought me a sled, brand new, in Boston where he'd been working. Home for Christmas. Two days is all my father got to be off. Took me on the sled down past the dump. Course it wasn't there, then."

Early touched the back of her arm and said, "Cold out, eh?"

"What are you doing here?"

He didn't have to say: bed sheet and underwear on the clothesline, Early barefoot in the snow without a shirt on.

"Get inside before you catch a cold."

He turned to say c'mon, Ol' Nip, because the dog usually came outside with Early to pee. Then he remembered.

Toby asked if Early knew how old he was today.

Without that back wall of D Jay's shed and a piece of chalk, it wasn't easy.

"You're eighteen."

Sounded like a lot of years going by he didn't remember, but not as many as Aubrey and Mrs. Aada had collected.

"Here, look what I got you. Mrs. Aada helped me."

Five Cherry Blossoms wrapped inside an old Moirs chocolate box.

"Meant to be six. Sorry, Early."

That's okay. He'd have given most of them to Toby anyhow.

Not today. This being Early's big day, Toby said he had to eat the most so Early had three and Toby only had two.

"You gonna be hungry for breakfast?"

You bet. Mrs. Aada'd been frying eggs and ham and potatoes at her house. Extra special because of two birthdays, the other being the Lord God baby Jesus.

"Maybe she'll have oranges."

"Yeah, oranges."

Aubrey greeted Toby with a Merry Christmas and a hug. Early, a Merry Christmas and a Happy Birthday handshake. Then it was outside to wash faces in the snow for Mrs. Aada's and going over to the church after.

"Early, you'll be needing your Christmas present."

Aubrey pulled a paper bag from atop the table under that tree.

"Santa Claus brought me somethin'?"

"Looks like he did."

New pants, shirt, and black shoes.

"You can touch them, Early, they won't break."

Aubrey told Toby, enough with the teasing. Early looked real nice dressed in his new clothes on his way out to milk Mrs. Trilby and to shovel a path to Mrs. Aada's. One more thing, Aubrey said. Santa left an apple on the table for the cow and Early was to give it to her.

Mrs. Aada did one fine breakfast that morning. Early ate three platefuls and Mrs. Aada was sure he was going to pop out of his Christmas clothes before the day was over.

"Don't be expecting his father to come by with new ones. I told you, Aubrey, that man's left the boy with you for good."

Aubrey told Early to ignore Mrs. Aada because those new clothes had lots of room to grow into. Even Toby ate lots, when he wasn't watching out the window.

Only one not hungry was Aubrey. Mrs. Aada should've had something to say about him staring at that empty spot by the stove, but she didn't. He was still missing Ol' Nip, that's all.

After breakfast, Mrs. Aada inspected, sending Early back for a comb, before everyone got ready for church. Walking over was not going to be easy, not with all that fresh snow, but the sun was out and it being winter, it was real nice just the same, folks saying Merry Christmas and how do.

"You know Early won't go inside," Toby said at the top of the church steps.

Deacon English was giving the service and it would be real nice.

"Won't hurt to come in on Christmas Day, Early," said Mrs. Aada. "Good singing this morning. Lot warmer too."

"D Jay says no."

Early didn't mind sitting on the steps like he always did, everyone inside, being toasty and happy. He could hear anyhow, was probably better off with that singing voice of his, and besides, Toby made him promise to keep his eyes open for Chub.

Mrs. Aada was doing a fine job going back and forth from the piano to the organ playing like she did and soon Early was singing right along with everyone inside: "King Jesus is a Listening," "Joy to the World," and "Glory Glory Hallelujah." Maybe because it was Christmas, no one stuck their head out the door and said shut your mouth, Early Okander. Folks passing on the road, like Blind Emmett and Mr. Sumlar and Larry Ganes coming by to see his dad, just said happy birthday, Early.

All that singing and it being Jesus's birthday and his, Early expected that when the service was over he was going to see a lot of happy faces. But the singing stopped and the doors stayed closed. Someone was talking, no way of knowing who it was, but must have been Deacon English. Early was shivering when everyone finally did come out. The ladies, some of them had tears. The men looked like they'd got punched, but didn't know by who. Aubrey was holding on tight to Toby, so Early asked how come?

"Everyone's saying this is our last Christmas. City's taking the houses."

"Don't you worry about that, Toby," said Aubrey. "I told you, come spring, moving talk'll go away like it always does."

Mrs. Aada was wiping her eyes with a tissue, then sticking it back in her purse.

"Not this time. I got a feeling."

Everyone else stepping out into that December cold must have felt the same thing.

Toby asked if Early'd seen Chub.

No.

Maybe she was waiting at the house.

Early hoped so. She'd put a smile on Toby for sure, and Early'd be glad to get away from the tears and that Charlie Savage starting to make snowballs.

"Early, what happens if we do have to move? Grandpa says you're a man now and if we go he can't take care of you."

Toby was up on Early's shoulders for the walk home.

"Pops'll come back."

"He's been gone a long time."

"Maybe he'll let me go with you."

A snowball caught Early dead centre on his back.

Toby wanted to wait a bit longer, but Mrs. Aada said the chicken was roasting to soup if it didn't get eaten soon.

"Your friend's got her family to be with today," said Aubrey. "You might not see her."

"But we got a present for her."

"Maybe she can't get away."

Toby had been watching at the window since getting back from church. Even made Early go up the lane to check if she was coming.

"Maybe she got stuck in the snow."

"I'll go look again."

"Don't talk so loose, Toby Daye, getting Early riled up with worry." Mrs. Aada was cooking dinner in Aubrey's kitchen on account of her empty store being where a Christmas table would go. But nothing was where it should be, it was way too small, and Lord knows it needed a woman's touch to keep it clean.

Aubrey winked at his grandson. Clearly missus was in need of Christmas cheer, so out came the bottle he saved for remembering days.

"Go on, Aada, it's Christmas."

Aubrey rested his hand on her shoulder when he said this, causing Toby to giggle and nudge Early in the ribs.

"Anyway, that Chub's smart enough to stay home if the snow's too deep," said Mrs. Aada, sipping her drink.

But they waited. Mrs. Aada set the table with Early and Toby helping. He insisted a place be set for Chub. Aubrey cranked the stove when it started to get dark, tapping it with his foot to hear how much oil was left, or maybe to drown out Mrs. Aada's peeling and mashing, and her saying it was all to be ruined if they didn't eat soon.

Then Toby, looking like someone cracked his head in two and poured the sun inside, danced around the kitchen.

"I see her!"

"Take it easy, son. That could be anyone out there."

"No, it's her! I know it's her."

Sure enough, with red cheeks, carrying her school bag.

"Oh, honey, what are you doing down here on an evening like this? All that snow out there."

Only Mrs. Aada could call Chub honey.

"Just bad walking from the end of Barrington Street."

"That's still a long way. You not having Christmas dinner with your family?"

Aubrey insisted Mrs. Aada let Chub take her coat off before all the questions.

"No, we had a big fight," said Chub. "My dad didn't want us worrying about Mom being sick in bed. He said we were going to have the best Christmas we ever had. He bought new lights for outside, but Mr. Venney said they were awfully bright and could my dad not put up so many. Aunt Joy got Mom's recipe box and made all kinds of pies and cookies, even chocolate chip ones and the butter ones you only get at Christmas, while she and my dad sang to these old Christmas songs on our hi-fi. But nothing tasted like my mom made them."

"That sounds real nice."

"But Mom was all by herself in her room. It's like she wasn't even there. Then my brother wanted to go over to Eddie's with his new Monopoly game. Dad said no. Aunt Joy's been cooking for days and we were having a family Christmas. Derek went anyhow, but Eddie's into hockey now and has hockey friends and told my brother he couldn't play 'cause they were going to some rink with their new skates. So Derek came back and slammed doors and said he hated everyone, and Dad said maybe Derek should play hockey too, toughen him up. That's when Aunt Joy cried."

"That's not very Christmasy, honey. Better get those snow pants off and come in and sit down."

"So when Leeza Jasmine called and said, 'Merry

Christmas, nigger-lover, heard your mom's croaking, guess that means you ate chicken for dinner last night 'cause I knew you were hatched from an egg,' I just said real loud, 'I'd love to have Christmas with you, thanks.' Should've heard her. My dad said go ahead because Christmas was ruined and no one was going to eat that turkey thawing in the sink, and we could all starve. But I know Derek's got lots of Oatmeal Creme Pies and RC Cola up in his room that he gets from his paper route money."

The tree drew her right over.

"It's beautiful."

Then she stuck her nose in and smelled the branches.

"Don't you have one at home?"

"Ours is fake. Looks like a toilet brush cleaner. Can't have a real tree or candles because they might go up in flames. I got presents."

Chub opened her school bag, gave Mrs. Aada hers first.

"They're bath beads. You put them in your bath and they melt and make your wrinkly skin all smooth."

"That's lovely. Thank you."

Early told Chub that Mrs. Aada didn't have a bathtub.

Aubrey's gift was a red handkerchief.

"It was for going around Ol' Nip's neck, so he'd look good for Christmas."

That was right thoughtful. Aubrey patted Chub on the arm.

She gave Early a chocolate bar.

"Only folks in heaven gets more chocolate than I got today."

That left Toby. Everyone sat around the tree waiting to see what fine thing Chub'd give him, they being special friends so of course the gift would be too, then they'd see the look on her face when she got her present. Toby was shaking when he opened the box Chub had wrapped in tin foil.

An orange crest with a bear wearing a Smokey hat.

"What does it say?"

"Indian River, Forest Rangers, Junior Division."

"It's just like mine, Toby. See?"

Chub pulled up her blouse to show her T-shirt riding up underneath with the same orange crest sewn on in the middle.

"You're a Junior Forest Ranger too."

Mrs. Aada asked Chub how she got those cut marks on her stomach, but Chub pulled down her T-shirt.

Toby was being very quiet, but Early knew he was about to explode from being happy.

"Give the young lady her gift," said Aubrey.

Toby handed her the box they'd all wrapped together. Chub said her brother took forever opening presents on Christmas morning, opening one side, then the other, then the top, then the bottom. Saved all the ribbon too.

"Not me." And she tore it open.

"See? You got to turn it and shake it like this," Early said, then showed her.

"It's got Ol' Nip and Mrs. Trilby too. And even your chickens, Early."

Chub put her arms around Toby.

Aubrey said it was time to eat, and getting up stiffly

from his chair, he waved Early into the kitchen to help Mrs.
Aada lift that heavy bird out of the oven.

The bird wasn't heavy at all, and Early said so, but
no one heard because Aubrey and Mrs. Aada were
whispering.

"It's nothing."

"You think so? The way they are together?"

"I know this, Aubrey Daye, you put your foot down,
it'll make it worse. Leave it be. It'll run its course. These
things do."

Mrs. Aada had Early walk Chub home after they all had
hot chocolate and Aubrey started yawning. The trains had
come through, clearing the tracks, making it the easiest
place to walk.

"You like that coat I gave you?"

"It's warm."

"This turned out to be my best Christmas ever." Chub
hugged her snow globe. "Now I'll be able to visit whenever
I want."

"I sure got lots of candy."

"You like that, huh?"

"Yeah. You think Pops'll come by?"

"Maybe. You know where he is?"

"Dunno. Been gone a long time."

"You lose things a lot up there." Meaning, in his head.

"Yeah, I guess."

Off the tracks and threading up the hill through drifts,

it was a good thing Chub had on her snow pants. At her house, the Christmas tree lights were already off.

"Tell Toby again, I really like my present."

"Okay."

"You sure you'll remember?"

"Yeah."

"Oh. Forgot. Happy birthday, Early."

She gave him a hug, then ran inside.

A city taxi was stuck in the snowbank by Aubrey's house when Early got back. The guy driving it was gunning the engine, digging the tires deeper. He asked, hey, buddy, gimme a push, which Early gave, and when he drove off after forgetting to say thanks, Early went inside.

Deborah had come 'round with boxes wrapped in coloured paper, tied with ribbons, now unwrapped and all over the floor. She'd given Toby a new car that worked with batteries and Aubrey a portable record player. Store-bought pants and shirts for her son with the tags still on them were folded on the table by empty beer bottles. Funny thing. With all that wonderful stuff, like a whole other Christmas had come, no one was looking very happy. Mrs. Aada had already gone home. She didn't stay around when Aubrey's girl came visiting.

"How'd you pay for all this?"

"For Christ's sake, Dad."

"Is that what this is from?"

"Do we have to have this conversation in front of the kid?"

"Why are you here?"

"It's Christmas. Can't I come by and see my boy?"

"It's just, we hardly see you, Deborah, and when we do, you're asking for money. So? What's it this time?"

Deborah went into the kitchen and opened another beer.

"You going to have one? I brought these for you."

"I don't want a drink. I want you to tell me why you're here."

"Fine. It's Knowl, if you must know."

"What's he done now?"

"I don't know, really, but the cops are looking for him and I don't want to get involved. Thought I'd stay here for a couple of days till things blow over." Toby got in the way. "Isn't it past your bedtime?"

Toby put his car down, took hold of Early's hand, and led him to his room. When he got into bed, he put his Forest Rangers crest on the side table so he could see it first thing when he got up.

"You have a good day, Early?"

"I like days with chocolate."

"Me too. And Chub."

"Hey, Toby, you like hearin' bad stuff about your dad?"

"Grandpa's my dad. Go to sleep, okay?"

In the dark, Early heard Toby open the bottle he kept by his bed, and smelled the bleach.

Not again.

Early stripped his bed and dropped his wet shorts. He pulled on his pants and slipped out of Toby's room.

"Can't sleep, baby?"

Deborah was smoking at the kitchen table. The lights were off. Early could only see the red tip of her cigarette.

"You know, Early, I feel really bad. I didn't bring you a present."

"It's okay. I got lots."

"No, it's not okay." She butted out her smoke on a saucer.

Deborah came over to the sink and slipped her arm around his waist. She smelled nice.

"I gotta wash my sheets."

"I'm going to give you a present. Normally costs a lot of money. Now we have to be real quiet. You don't want to wake Toby, do you?"

"No."

She unzipped his pants and pushed them down around his ankles.

"Sure you don't wanna come and work with me at the hotel?"

"Leave Toby and Aubrey?"

"That so bad?"

"I don't want to go."

She had his cock in her hands and was getting him hard. Never took much. Then she got on her knees and put him into her mouth, her head bobbing up and down. Felt good. Sometimes, buddies that paid D Jay to have a go at him, that's all they wanted to do until they came in his mouth. He didn't know if Deborah wanted that, so when he was close, he said so.

"Remember, baby—quiet."

Deborah got up and opened her robe. She took Early's cock and slid it up and down in front of her until it slipped inside, then she pushed Early back against the sink so she could sit on his thighs and jack herself up and down.

"Jesus," she said, forgetting about being quiet, but clamping her hand over Early's mouth. Good thing. He made a lot of noise.

"Merry Christmas, baby."

Early pulled up his pants, went outside, and hung up the bedsheet.

MRS. AADA SAVED CARDBOARD BOXES FROM HER store so Early and Toby could go sledding on Uncle Laffy's Hill. But first, she sent them to check on Old Irene. Irene Battle lived alone and the last few days had been cold. Her place was in behind the church, across the tracks. Tucked in among her neighbours and a bunch of sheds, it was a squat house with a red tarpaper roof patched so often it looked to Early like it was bleeding from the seams. Irene tried her best to make it over, but she pretty much didn't get out of her chair by the oil stove.

Irene sent the boys to have a look at the crawl space. Should be banked with dirt and straw to keep out drafts, Early said. Then she offered them a cup of hot Oxo. She said that's what Joe Louis liked to sip on, a cup of hot Oxo, first thing in the morning. Old Irene couldn't remember who she'd told, how often, or how long ago the boxer had shown up on her doorstep looking for a place to stay.

"Real nice, that Mr. Louis. Came up to Halifax to do

some refereeing, but you know, boys, when he found out his hotel didn't take coloureds, but they'd take him, being so famous and all, he said no thanks and got himself down to Africville."

Early asked D Jay about that when he first heard the story. D Jay was pretty much a know-it-all when it came to sports, but he couldn't remember ever hearing about Joe Louis being in town. But as far as the bit about the hotel went, everyone knew monkeys couldn't afford them.

Lots of kids were out sledding already, the day being not too cold, fog hanging over the harbour. Fog came sometimes in winter, mixing everything up like one big bowl of cloud soup. Then the wind blew in the sun.

Toby had to beat his record each time, ending up past the stop of the last run. Let's try and hit the water. That was what he said, but he didn't really mean it because who wanted to go swimming in a cold harbour? It meant climbing the hill as high as they could go, whistling down between houses and sheds and shitters, not forgetting to duck under Mrs. Jensen's frozen-stiff dresses and dish towels hanging across the hill.

Toby sat on the box up front, Early in behind. Other kids made fun, saying Early was too big to go sledding with Toby, but like Toby told them, no rule says you can't.

After going up and down the hill three times, Toby got winded and Early lost the hat and mittens Aubrey had lent him.

Deacon English was down by the road in back of the church, waving.

"You come with me, Early," he said, nice like, not in that church voice of his.

"Just one more slide?"

"No, son. There's some men come to see you."

"Who wants to see Early?"

"Policemen, Toby. They're with your grandfather right now."

"How come?"

"Why not let them talk to Early?" asked the deacon.

That got the boys finished up with sledding, especially when Toby got sent to bring the boxes back to Mrs. Aada's.

"Early, you remember finding that seal?" Deacon English asked on the way to Aubrey's.

"Yeah."

"Take an angry man, hurt a seal."

Not right doing that.

"You got something you want to tell me about your dad before we get back?"

"Pops is workin'. He'll come back."

"I know what kind of man your father was, Early. People would understand. If there's anything, anything at all, now's the time to tell me. I can't help you after. Maybe I can now."

"You think I done somethin'?"

"Just making sure."

The car parked outside of Aubrey's was not one of those city police cars with flashing lights, but an all black one. Maybe Deacon English got it wrong and it wasn't the police. Chub's dad drove a car like that when he came to play cards.

Mrs. Aada and Aubrey and Toby were sitting at the kitchen table looking like maybe they did something wrong. First time Early'd ever seen Mrs. Aada sitting down there and not fussing around, making tea or something. Two men in dark suits stood by the oil stove.

"Here he is," said Deacon English. "This is Early Okander."

Mrs. Aada was all wet around the eyes, but she'd been that way since Christmas.

"Early, these men have come about your father."

"Pops?"

The taller of the two said Daniel Joseph, Dusty Joe, D Jay, or what's left of him, had washed ashore on George's Island in Halifax Harbour. Apparently Early's dad collected names.

"Oh."

"When's the last time you saw him?"

Maybe Toby could help. Early didn't have anything to count with.

"When was the last time you saw your father, huh?"

"Early's not good at remembering things."

"Nice. Is he stupid, or just retarded?"

"It's the way he was born."

"That's just great."

"You don't think Early had something to do with this?" asked Deacon English.

"The kid doesn't look too broken up over his old man being shot."

Toby explained that Early didn't know what being dead meant. He sometimes expected Ol' Nip to come waddling through the front door.

The other fellow, the one who'd kept his mouth shut all this time, was writing in a paper book with a coil spine along the top. He showed something he'd written to his buddy.

"How about Knowl Manzer, old man? You know where he is?"

Aubrey said he hadn't seen his son-in-law in months.

"Son-in-law, eh? For real, or is this what you're calling it?"

"Deborah and Knowl were married in that church over there, so I expect if it's good enough for God, it'll do for everyone else."

"Where's she now?"

"Was here for Christmas. Stayed till New Year's."

"Heard from her since?"

"No."

Deacon English wanted to know what Knowl and Deborah had to do with D Jay.

"Manzer and Okander are well known to us. What's the wife doing?"

Like Aubrey already said, he didn't know.

"You know she's a working girl by the train station?"

"Is this necessary in front of the boys?" asked Deacon English.

"When a body washes up like it did, it's necessary."

"I don't know where my daughter is. That's the truth."

Buddy writing stopped writing.

"You're going to give me a call if you hear from her, or you see your son-in-law, got that?"

Aubrey got it.

"You know you can go to jail if you're hiding them."

"If Mr. Daye says he doesn't know, he doesn't."

The two policemen seemed to think Deacon English was being funny because they laughed before they left, not out loud so everyone could hear, but to each other.

Mrs. Aada borrowed a suit for Early from Mr. Ganes, but it was kind of tight. Larry wasn't as big as Early. Mrs. Aada said it'd do because Early had to look proper when they went to Fairview Cemetery.

Aubrey and Toby got dressed up as well. Deacon English took them and Mrs. Aada in his car. She was saying it was a damn shame this happened to Early and to have to see his father buried in a pauper's grave.

Toby kept asking if Early was all right, and don't be sad. But he wasn't. All Early cared about was asking Chub to come along, but Mrs. Aada said no, not this time.

So they went and watched a big box get buried in the ground. Mrs. Aada had the lid removed for Early to have a look. Said he needed closure. Looked like a dead seal to Early and he'd already seen that one before. After, Deacon

English took them for milkshakes. Early had a chocolate one. Toby had strawberry, but he started to cry and couldn't finish his. Mrs. Aada told Early to take off his jacket just in case he spilled milkshake on it.

When they got back from the cemetery, Miss Ruby from the post office was waiting. Maybe she'd been waiting for a long time because she was hopping around in the cold.

"Why weren't you at the church meeting last night?"

"Oh, Ruby, we've been getting Early's father buried. You know they found him, eh? Forgot all about it."

"City's done it. They're moving us."

Miss Ruby handed a letter to Deacon English.

The meeting was to discuss the report Dr. Rose put together telling the city don't you be spending any more time asking questions about getting folks out of Africville.

"He said the city should tear it down. A civilized society wouldn't allow us to live that way. They held a vote at the church last night about staying or going."

"How many people voted?"

"Maybe thirty or more, Aada. Claimed it was enough."

"Enough? With all the people living here?"

"Ma, calm down. Let me find out some things first."

"That's right, missus. Gotta be an explanation for this," said Aubrey.

Deacon English took the letter Miss Ruby gave him and hurried over to the church. He had a telephone in there, so he could make calls.

"Now what good is that? What can we do?"

"Pray!" he shouted back.

Toby said, "C'mon, Early, let's go see Mrs. Trilby."

Chub hadn't been around since Christmas, so she didn't know about them burying Early's dad, and Early and Toby didn't know when they'd see her again. With all the news, they couldn't wait. Toby remembered Chub saying her aunt was working for the city. Maybe if she knew how much everyone wanted to stay, she could talk to whoever was running things.

Should they go back to Chub's school and wait for her there?

No. It was January. Too cold, too far.

After a lot of one-sided talk, they decided to go to her house and try to say hey.

Good thing some windy days had come and moved around the snow. It made getting Toby up the hill to Chub's a lot easier, after Early got over the drifts. Early was good at throwing snowballs, better than Toby, so he'd throw one at her window, softly, didn't want to break it, just to let her know company was calling.

It took a couple of tries before she pulled the curtains. Toby waved.

"Hey."

Hey back.

"I'm doing my homework."

"I'm here too."

"Hi, Early. Whatcha doing?"

"D Jay got washed up on an island."

"Drowned?"

Early nodded.

"My mom says only thing worse than getting burned is getting drowned, 'cause her cousin fell through the ice and floated to Montreal." Chub promised to say a whole rosary for D Jay, if she could find it.

Toby let her know about the vote for moving people out of Africville. Could Chub talk to her aunt because if she knew how much people wanted to stay, and said so, maybe she could change things?

"What's your grandpa say?"

"Oh, he's telling Miss Portia right away in another letter because she knows the Queen and maybe she can get the Queen to help."

"Queen's a good idea."

"Could take a while. She's in England."

"Okay. I'll talk to my aunt. I still got my snow globe."

"Yeah?"

"I shake it every night before I go to bed."

Toby unzipped his coat and showed her the shirt Aubrey had sewn his Junior Rangers crest on.

Toby didn't say anything until they got over the train tracks, then he climbed down from Early's back and started walking.

"Thanks for taking me."

"Sure."

"Chub and me's a Forest Ranger. We'll get this fixed."

﹡⌒

Early thought it real nice of Toby's mom to come by and help Aubrey sort things out, after reading in the paper the city was clearing out Africville.

"Thanks a lot, Dad, for telling the cops where I was."

"How could I do that? I never know where you are. You in some kind of trouble?"

"Not me. That Knowl again. Who the devil knows where he is and I sure as hell don't know anything about what happened to D Jay. Told that to the cops, but I doubt they believe me. Jesus, Dad, what the hell have you got up here?"

Deborah was tiptoeing on a step ladder, looking into the crawl space over the living room ceiling.

"Been putting stuff up there for years and forgetting about it."

She made Early go up, start bringing down all the boxes.

"How else are we going to find that deed?"

"I told you, I'll look for it."

"When? City comes and bulldozes this place down on top of you? Not a chance. I'm not leaving till I got it. Toby, you get sifting through those boxes Early gives you."

He wanted to know what he was looking for.

"Anything that proves we own this piece of shit."

✺

Next hallelujah day when Early was listening to the singing, waiting for Aubrey and Mrs. Aada and Toby to finish up inside the church, he watched Chub coming down the road with a suitcase. It was big and awkward and kept banging against her knees.

"You wanna listen to the singin' with me?"

Chub shook her head.

"Really sorry about your dad, Early."

"Yeah."

"I dreamt my mom died and Dad made me stand by the door and make people sign the guest book. They could eat smoked meat sandwiches in the basement if they didn't want to look at Mom. I didn't even recognize her. Her hair got permed like that Marg on *Don Messer's Jubilee*. I hate that show. Then me and Derek sat in the bleachers across the street to get some air that didn't smell of dead people and lots of flowers. I cried when I woke up."

"You got a suitcase, huh?"

"I'm going to Indian River."

"How come?"

Chub put down her case and joined Early, back against the door.

"Because it's all my fault."

She sniffled. Chub never cried.

"I asked Aunt Joy, like you and Toby wanted. She said there's nothing she'd do, even if she could. Said she was being a good Christian by getting you to go 'cause you're living like pigs down here and that makes people in the city all ashamed. She goes, for God sakes, Penny, they don't even have toilets. Why is everyone so worried about toilets? My Uncle Jack in Shubenacadie doesn't have one. He's got an outhouse, but I guess that's different. Aunt Joy says people like Toby and his grandpa and Mrs. Aada can't take care of themselves, so someone has to, and the city wants this land for factories. What about Mrs. Trilby and you and Aubrey and Mrs. Aada and Toby and swimming and all that good stuff and that you don't want to go, but she says public housing is better. You'll get real toilets."

"That right then, about goin'?"

Chub wiped her eyes with the back of her arm.

"Even Mrs. Trilby?"

"If I hadn't come here to take that stupid picture, maybe Aunt Joy wouldn't want you to go. I hate her. She'll be sorry when I'm a Ranger in Indian River. And on TV."

"That's a long way?"

Very far. Chub picked up her case, and continued banging her knees down the road.

Everyone coming out of the church that morning was catching Chub's tears. Toby said it was because they couldn't stop talking about the city finally deciding to tear down Africville.

"Chub's sad about that too."

"Yeah?"

"Uh huh. Told me when she come by."

"When?"

"Waitin' for you. Said it was her fault. That's why she's gonna be a Ranger. With a suitcase."

If Chub was going, they were bound to go with her.

"What about Mrs. Aada cookin' for us now?"

"Are you coming?"

Without anyone knowing what they were doing, Early got the wagon for Toby to sit in. Good thing Chub had her heavy suitcase and was slow walking. She wasn't even across the train tracks where the road was paved and the plow stopped.

Toby hollered and waved. Early too.

"Where you going?"

"Indian River where the Rangers are. I hate it at my house. I hate them all. If they won't let you stay here, I'm going."

"Won't they miss you?"

"I don't care."

Chub went back to walking, and knocking.

"You coming back?"

"I dunno. Could be far."

"Can me and Early come?"

Chub moved her mouth around on her face, thinking about it.

"Okay."

Chub got in the wagon beside Toby and put her suitcase across their knees. Early pulled.

"Gonna have to get money," she said. "You know, for the trip."

"We'll all get jobs."

"I got one already. I work for Mr. Welford."

"No, Early. Not anymore."

Chub thought she might drive a bus, and Toby was sure he could bag groceries. Then they could cut down trees and build their own fort in the woods, just like the Forest Rangers, in case it was too far to get to the real one. Early could be Indian Joe.

"Good idea," said Toby.

An idea that needed lots of plans and rules about who'd do what and who'd be top dog running the new fort and maybe they could get on TV too.

But it was getting cold and starting to snow.

"You all right, Toby?"

He nodded, or maybe it was shivering. At least Early got to keep warm by walking and pulling.

"I bet it'd be okay to go after eating at Mrs. Aada's. You could come too, Chub."

"What about our fort?"

"We gotta get something to cut down trees."

Chub thought that was a good idea so Early turned the wagon around.

CHUB SAID SHE WAS GOING TO BE SAMUEL DE Champlain in her school's spring pageant. Richmond School where Toby went didn't do that kind of thing, but that fancy school of Chub's put on shows.

"It's about the founding of Canada and I get to be a boy."

"How come?"

"Because there's no boys in my school."

"You be on TV?"

"No, not that kind show. It's on a stage."

"You get to say anything?"

"It's called a tableau. I stand there for five minutes, frozen, like in a picture."

"Doing what?"

"Subjugating the natives."

"What's that mean?"

"Don't you know anything, Toby?"

Sounded like Chub didn't know either. Then she handed over four tickets, one for Early and Toby and Mrs. Aada and Aubrey. Toby didn't care for Aubrey saying they couldn't go, but it was real nice of Chub to get the tickets. She came back later and brought her costume over and put it on, then stood on the footstool in Aubrey's living room with her hands outstretched, head high, face like Mrs. Briscoe, showing them what her part was. That kind of made up for missing the performance.

"How come Mrs. Aada's not here?" Chub asked, pulling off her long costume robe in Toby's room.

"They're not talking."

"Why?"

"Something about a deed, I dunno," said Toby. "Hey, how'd you get those?"

Little cuts all in a row up and down her arms. Some old and scarred, some looking fresh. Chub tried to hide them.

"That kid, Leeza, do that to you?"

"No."

"You want a bandage or something?"

"Shut up, Toby, stop looking." Then she got right sorry, seeing what yelling did to Toby. "Sometimes I get mad about things, and this makes me feel better."

"You do that?"

"You won't tell?"

"Naw. You don't get mad here, do you?"

Chub smiled.

Early liked it when lupins finally covered the hills with patches of pink and white and yellow and blue that swayed when the wind blew. Didn't have to rub that much sleep out of his eyes getting up to milk Mrs. Trilby. Sometimes birds were up too, but mostly it was quiet. No cars, tires grinding up gravel on the road, no folks out saying how do, Early. Sometimes the only sound was a bedsheet snapping on a laundry line, maybe a dog barking. And Mrs. Trilby saying get yourself over here, Early, and milk me. Not said like that with words, more like just a grunt. A loud one.

Then came the morning when the quiet got broken. First time was over at Mrs. Jensen's. She had that bungalow up the road, other side of the tracks. Could see it from Aubrey's and Mrs. Aada's. Nice little place, had shutters on the windows decorated with half moons. In the summer, Mrs. Jensen's roses and morning glories grew up and over the window boxes.

Early was standing on the porch with the bucket for Mrs. Trilby when he heard the roar, like a truck having a cough, getting started up. One minute there's Mrs. Jensen's place, next minute, there's a tractor, shovel on the front, riding right over it.

Gone.

Bringing down that first house got Aubrey and Toby up real fast and they came out to have a see for themselves. Mrs. Aada too, wearing her housecleaning kerchief, peeking outside her door.

Mrs. Jensen had come by the other day to tell Aubrey that she'd been visiting with Mr. Selby. He was the social worker from the city come to work things out with folks about going. Mrs. Jensen said he was real nice and polite, came into her kitchen and had a cup of tea.

Mrs. Jensen, she was all by herself now, no man to live with, no kids. Like she said to Aubrey, I'm too old to get water from wells. Mr. Selby told her she'd get a nice place in Mulgrave Park with a washing machine. City'd give her five hundred dollars, which was nice because she didn't own that place she was in, and could pay off a bill she had at the hospital for being in there last year when her heart started skipping beats. Besides, that house of hers needed a new roof she couldn't afford. What else could she do?

Aubrey told her to say no. Can't do nothing if we all stand together.

The city moved Mrs. Jensen real fast after she made up her mind. One day you sign a paper, next day your house is gone. Poor Mrs. Jensen cried like a baby when that happened. She was second thinking about selling, but Aubrey said it was because no city movers'd come down to Africville, too scared, and poor Mrs. Jensen had to go like garbage on the back of a city dump truck.

Standing out there, watching that tractor ride over Mrs. Jensen's house, Early saw on Aubrey and Toby and Mrs. Aada's faces what he felt inside. A piece of something good was taken.

Aubrey and Mrs. Aada's not talking started after Deborah came looking for the deed. When she had Early clean out the crawl space so she could go through every box, most of it she said was junk and needed to be in the dump, Deborah said her father didn't have a deed. That's when she marched over to Mrs. Aada's and had a talk.

If something was lost at Aubrey's, chances are Mrs. Aada'd find it. She liked to say she knew where every minute of her life was, and probably everyone else's. Told that to Aubrey when she had a go about his shabby housekeeping. Sure, she had papers, lots of them. Turns out she had one about Aubrey too, a real old one, looked like it spent time in the bottom of a teapot. Guess what? Deborah asked her father. Aubrey owned his house, but the land was Mrs. Aada's.

"That can't be right. My daddy gave me this place."

"What he gave you was this shack, worth almost nothing."

"So? I'm not going anywhere."

"What if she sells out?"

Aubrey had known Mrs. Aada for a long, long time, and words between her and his daughter weren't going to cause trouble between them. That was okay until Mrs. Aada starting sounding like maybe they should give up and go, like the city wanted, get into a new place. The city's going to get what the city wants, Mrs. Aada kept saying whenever she and Aubrey talked about it. Aubrey didn't think so. The solution was simple: Mrs. Aada had to sell him the land his house was on. She could go to the devil after that. He'd hold his ground, even if he was the last one.

No way was Mrs. Aada ever going to sell any land, except maybe to the city. This news came from Toby. He told Early it was because if she goes, she'll want Aubrey to go with her.

❦

Aubrey came into Toby's room with a handful of towels and stuck them around the windowsill to keep out the rain. Waves were washing over the road down by the church, he said. Could Early go tie up Mrs. Trilby inside Jubilee Hall so nothing would get blown on her during the night?

When Early came back, he unbuttoned his shirt and pulled it off, then he used it to dry off his dripping face and hair.

"It's bad, huh?"

"You gonna be afraid, Toby?"

"No. I'm glad it's storming. Tractors won't come tonight."

When they did, might wake up and find Mr. Ganes was gone. Blind Emmett too. Nothing but dirt where they used to live. What if the tractors came and knocked down their house while they were sleeping?

"That what you scared about?"

"No...going."

"Your grandpa says we won't."

"I don't mean us. Everyone else. They're all fighting about the money they're getting, not about staying, like Grandpa says we gotta. We'll be down here all by ourselves."

"Still got Mrs. Trilby and Mrs. Aada. Chub'd come."

"Yeah, maybe. But right now, everyone living here's the same. Except you."

They saw Chub on their way to the dump, pedalling her bike real fast. Coming round the turn, she raised her hands in the air and yahooed. She didn't know the puddle she was riding into was going to go up to her knees. About halfway in, her bike tipped over and Chub got both her feet wet.

"Toby, I'm going back to Richmond School, same as you."

"Huh?"

"My dad says Sacred Heart costs too much."

Sun came out right there, even if it was only on Toby's face.

Early asked Chub, did she see? There were branches and roof shingles sprinkled all over from the storm last night, and there was a puddle in Mrs. Aada's back yard Aubrey said looked deep enough to swim in. Mrs. Trilby did okay, but she made a fuss to get outside after the wind blew a piece off Jubilee Hall and almost hit her, so Aubrey wanted them to go find a patch.

"I'll help."

On the way back from getting the wagon filled with wood, Toby counted the houses that were gone.

"That's a lot," said Chub.

When Early climbed the ladder to the roof to see about fixing the hole, Toby wanted to go up too, have a look. That meant Toby and Chub.

"Grandpa, look."

Toby waved, sitting beside Chub, and said he could see lots, like that man coming by. The man shouted a how-do, said he was Mr. Selby from the city. It being hot out as the day after a storm can be, he had his jacket slung over his shoulder, but he did have his white shirt and tie on. That meant he was on the clock, Mr. Daye, and shook his hand. Too bad the road was still muddy, made a mess of those brown tie-ups of his.

"Got yourself some damage last night, I see."

"Yes, sir. Get it fixed right up."

"That your boy up there? Looks like he's got himself too much sun."

"My grandson, Toby. Chub, that's his friend. And Early stays with us now."

"Interesting building you got there. Is that a cow?"

Early shouted down that it was for Miss Portia White. The building, not the cow.

"Oh, she from around here?"

Aubrey didn't look to care much for Mr. Selby.

"I had a visit this morning with your neighbour over there, Mrs. Dupuis."

"You've been talking to Mrs. Aada?"

"Then I guess you know why I'm here."

Aubrey turned and waved to Early, said bring those kids down and be careful.

Mr. Selby from the city smiled. Had his hands over the fence watching Toby on the ladder.

"I'm not going," said Aubrey.

Being on the roof is how Early got to see Miss Ruby coming out of her house with that brown envelope, waving it in air, calling Aubrey! but sounding like Fire! Fire! She had to bend over to catch her breath, still holding up that envelope, when she came by.

"It's...for you...Aubrey."

Mr. Selby nodded to the postmistress, folded his jacket back over his other arm, and walked to Deacon English's place. Early thought about saying he was gone, left that morning, but big news, really big news, got in the way.

"Is it...is it from her?" asked Miss Ruby.

Early could see Aubrey trembling even from up the ladder.

"I think so."

"Open it, Grandpa."

"Now wait just a minute. Early, go get Mrs. Aada. She's been expecting this too."

Chub was dancing up and down on her feet, holding onto Toby's back.

"Miss Ruby, you coming inside while I open this?"

"Try and stop me. I've been waiting for this as long as you have."

Early went yelling for Mrs. Aada, banging on her door,

telling her that a letter'd come from Miss Portia White, and they were all waiting over at Aubrey's for her so it could be opened.

When they were all crowded around the table in Aubrey's kitchen, him sitting, that envelope flat out in front, Mrs. Aada told him to get on with it, old man.

Aubrey nodded at Toby, and thanked Jesus. Only right when a prayer was answered. Then he opened the letter.

Chub spoke first. "That her? She's beautiful."

No letter, but in the photograph that came, she sure was. *For my biggest fan, Aubrey Daye.* Signed, *Portia White.*

Miss Ruby went back home to look for another letter, just in case it went astray, but everyone knew she'd never lost a single piece of mail in all the years she ran the post office.

Mrs. Aada was sure she could hear disappointment all over Africville. Her ears must have been real good because Early didn't hear a thing. The house was very quiet after Aubrey opened that letter. Missus wanted to know if anyone was hungry for supper, but Chub had to go home for hers and Aubrey said no thanks, and went to bed. So Mrs. Aada made Early and Toby hot chicken with gravy over bread and let them split a Pepsi left in her store.

"Clean up those dishes when you're finished, Toby, so your grandfather doesn't wake up to a messy kitchen."

That's how Mrs. Aada and Aubrey made up.

Early was sorry.

"It's not your fault."

"But your grandpa's sad."

"Maybe Chub's right. Could be another letter coming."

Better hurry if that was the case. Old Irene's and Molasses Jack's houses were gone and LaVerna Taylor's girls helped move her out, day before. By the time Miss Portia got to Africville, no one'd be there.

"Here, I'm not hungry."

"You sure?"

"Yeah. I'm tired."

That left Early sitting at the kitchen table, eating for two.

NEXT MORNING EARLY WANTED TO KNOW IF
Toby was up for going back on the roof and helping.

"Naw. I'll sit on the porch so's you can talk to me."

That's what they did, Early talking to Toby, Toby talking
back. Mrs. Aada put sheets on the line, came over and said
hello, went in to see Aubrey.

"Hey, Toby, you sleepin'?"

"A little bit. I'm really hot."

Early thought he was just joking because Toby was
lying in the shade and there was a good breeze coming off
the harbour. Not freezing cold, but sure enough, not hot.

"You want me to get you somethin'? Water?"

"I'm okay."

Early got back to hammering and talking, Toby saying,
yes or no, and pretty soon that hole got patched in the roof.
That left only Early talking to Toby down on the porch
with his eyes closed.

"Hey, you are sleepin'."

No answer this time as Early got down from the ladder to check. Better off in bed than lying on the porch, so Early picked him up and carried him inside.

"Toby fell asleep," he said to Aubrey and Mrs. Aada.

The old folks were sitting at the kitchen table, staring at a pot of tea and empty cups. Missus took one look at Toby and put her hands around his face.

"He's on fire."

They got Toby into bed and Mrs. Aada went to her place for rubbing alcohol to break the fever, but as soon as she put it on Toby's peeling-off skin, he screamed. Then Mrs. Aada got cold water and towels and everyone took turns trying to get Toby to cool down.

Next morning, Toby was a bit better when Chub came by, but no getting out of bed. Doctor Aada's orders. Chub read from one of Toby's Jalna books and said she liked that fella Finch. Toby laughed and made her read parts over. That's as well as he got. Day after that, Toby was still in bed, hot all over again and throwing up.

Aubrey and Mrs. Aada had that look on their faces, like someone pushing down the top of their heads. Lots of whispering too that Early couldn't hear. Next visit from Chub, Aubrey wouldn't let her in while Toby was still being sick, so maybe she should stay home. He told Early he couldn't sleep in the same room anymore, just until they knew what was wrong, make sure nobody catches anything.

If Early couldn't see Toby, he could talk to him. At night, when Aubrey was asleep, he sat against Toby's door and told him about milking Mrs. Trilby, like he always did, fixing Jubilee Hall and it being all done now, and no more worrying about Charlie Savage and Tom Reed, their places got pulled down.

"You hear that, Toby?"

"Yeah."

Chub was as good at listening to Aubrey as she was to her folks. Next time she came back, she had a bunch of daisies picked by the prison fields. Everyone knew they grew real thick up there. D Jay told Early that was because Rockhead guards beat young boys to death that got sent there, and buried them in the middle of the night. Made for good fertilizer.

"Can I give them to Toby?"

Mrs. Aada was making a tray of tea and toast. His grandpa was sitting by the bed.

"They're lovely, dear. You get them in some water and let me see how Toby's doing first."

The daisies had ants and when Early was at the counter helping Chub pick them off, something got broken inside Toby's room and Mrs. Aada was at the door looking God-awful worried.

"Early, go get Deacon English."

"Is Toby okay?"

"Hurry."

Only thing, Deacon English wasn't home. Knock and knock and knock—no answer.

Mrs. Aada didn't care for that news. She practically yelled at Chub to go home, now. Early was to stay out on the porch. They did as they were ordered, but not before they heard Aubrey calling from inside Toby's room, saying that Toby couldn't move his arms or legs.

Mrs. Aada had Early stay with her at her place. Whatever Toby had, it was bad, and he might catch it. He didn't care about that. Maybe if he got it, it'd leave Toby alone. He sure didn't like disrespecting Mrs. Aada, he'd never done that before, she being so good to him, but when she fell asleep, he got back into Aubrey's house and sat against Toby's door. Poor old man. Taking care of his grandson had tuckered him right out. He was too tired to even get up off the sofa, sleeping where he sat.

Early wasn't. That was how he heard the stones getting thrown against the kitchen window. Little ones. Tick tick tick.

"I see you there, Early." Chub was talking through the screen. "Let me in. I got something for Toby."

They had to be real quiet, seeing Aubrey sleeping over there.

"Mrs. Aada said stay away."

"I don't care."

Inside, Chub opened Toby's door. The room stunk, like after Early wet the bed. Toby was sleeping. Chub started to cry. A little bit at first, then lots more the harder she tried not to.

"I told my aunt what was wrong with Toby and that he needed help. She got so mad at me. Said after everything they'd done for me, Mom and Dad letting me come back to my old school, and I was still coming down here with you guys. She's gonna tell Dad to put bars on my windows and too bad if there's a fire and I can't get out. But I said Toby couldn't walk and she got scared, Early. Really scared. Said it was polio, and it was a good thing I got vaccinated because people die from polio and if they're lucky, they never walk again. Good thing my rope ladder for in case of fire works for running away."

"That you, Chub?"

Sure was good to hear Toby.

"Look what I got for you. Aunt Joy helped me get it because I said I needed it for school. It's brand new, well, from the second-hand store, but no one's read it yet. You'll be the first."

She turned on the light by the bed. "Sorry," she said, because she could see that it hurt his eyes.

Toby ran his fingers over the book's green cover, his mouth silently speaking.

"It's *Centenary at Jalna*, Toby, by Mazo de la Roche. Now you'll find out what happens to those Whiteoaks you like. Hey, Toby, how about I read some?"

He nodded.

"Wish I helped you finish the roof, Early."

"That's okay. You'll be better soon. I heard your grandpa and Mrs. Aada talkin' about gettin' money from that Mr. Selby."

"He say that, Early? You sure?"

"Yeah, to make you feel better."

"Early, no, he can't. That means he'll have to go. Grandpa's lived his whole life here. He'll hate being in that park place."

"No way, Toby. He's just gettin' money, not movin'."

"Oh, Early."

"How about I read now?"

Chub did, but Toby didn't look to care much about those Whiteoaks. Early got tired after that, being up so long worrying, and slept by Toby for a bit. Coming to, he heard Chub and Toby talking softly.

"Wish I could get to the pond and lay in the water. I'd feel good."

"We could do it. Me and Early can carry you."

"What about Grandpa?"

"We'll go out the window."

Chub offered to help, but Early knew all about carrying Toby. Been doing it for a long time. Good thing there was a big moon making them able to see, and only crickets for company.

"Tibby's Pond, Early. Let's go there."

So they did and when they got to the water, Toby wanted to get right in.

"Me too."

Toby said that would be okay, but Early should take off his clothes. Chub came too.

"I don't care if I get wet."

Toby had been sweating so much his pyjamas were soaking. Early lay him in the water, not deep, and held him. Toby smiled.

"Thanks, Early."

At first, the water was cold, but you could get used to it and Early started nodding off again holding Toby for so long, hearing only pieces of things.

"I can't let Grandpa move...Chub can hold me."

So Early let her float Toby from his arms.

When the sun found them, Early and Toby were lying on the sandy part of the pond. Tide was out. Chub must've went home. Deacon English came looking. Everyone was worried about Toby not being in his bed.

It's okay, Early told him. Toby was feeling much better. He wasn't hot anymore.

WHEN EARLY LOOKED BACK AT HOW FAR HE'D
come, Mrs. Aada's voice in his head was saying you got to
plant 'em straight, Early. But these fields were bigger than
the garden patch behind Mrs. Trilby's pen, and potatoes
had a mind of their own.

He'd start over.

Early liked being in these fields. His back browned easily
under the sun after being inside for so long. No hearing all
those noises, like the walls got a heartbeat going too fast,
grown men crying. Outside meant no one laughed at you
while you mopped floors and maybe tip over your bucket,
or paint you up with whitewash instead of the walls.

Before he got into the fields Early sat all day in a narrow
hall outside the rooms with benches and a sink on the wall
the other men spit in, and because he ruined his mattress,
he had to sleep on planks. Early got pains in his back, but
better that than getting bit all night from what crawled
around inside the stuffing. Then one day the man at his
gate told Early he'd been real good, minding himself,

saying sir when he's supposed to, waiting in his underwear at the bars each morning wanting to please-can-I-wash-my-piss-soaked sheets, so they were going to let him carry a shovel.

The man leaning on the fence watching him now said no one grew better-tasting potatoes than Early. Even his wife said bring me some of that boy's spuds. Must be because of Early going up and down those rows of plants, sometimes on his knees, picking away at bugs eating the leaves and sticking them in his pocket for Chub. Maybe she could get jars and lettuce for them all and tell him what kind they were. But most times he forgot he was carrying them until he got back inside and his pocket was all squishy. So Early found an old soup can and kept the slugs and caterpillars in there. But Chub never came around and when the bugs died, Early put them down the toilet.

The only thing he didn't like about working in the fields was having to put away the wheelbarrow. Going into that stone shed, dead flies dying on top of one another along the sill, made Early think about that other shed, one that had six dead babies lying in a trench. None of them had heads, but they did have wings and when they saw Early they flew around him until he woke up at night calling for Toby, and the man on the top bunk telling him to shut the fuck up.

When he could see from the fields the new bridge starting to come, Early wondered if Toby could see that from his grandpa's house, and maybe it would be a good place to keep Mrs. Trilby underneath so she wouldn't get wet, like when the storms came. The man on the fence who watched him, he'd just scratch his head and grin and tell Early to get back into it. But Early didn't mind that fella. He wasn't like that little man with the thin sideburns who sat beside Early at the table all those days before they brought him here. That man didn't like Early fidgeting and kept telling him he didn't care if the collar was too tight, Early had to keep his top button done up or it might look disrespectful to his honour, and Early was in enough trouble as it was. Every time Early moved, the man gave him a pinch that left black marks up and down his arm. He finally gave Early a pencil and some paper and told him to pretend he was writing because he knew Early couldn't.

Sometimes when Early was bent down in the potatoes, kids'd come by, climb on the fence, and make a game of throwing stones to see who could hit him. Early always asked if they knew Chub or Toby. The kids on the fence would just laugh and make piggy noises because they said Early looked like one with his nose in the dirt, then they'd run away.

Once, he saw a woman walking slow on the road. She was big like Mrs. Aada and had swollen ankles, and she carried two heavy bags. But when Early went over to the fence to say hello, he saw that the woman wasn't Mrs. Aada. She tried to run and apples fell out of one of her bags. The man watching him told Early if he did that again, he'd not be let back out into the fields.

When the potato plants got flowers on them, Early'd hide a small handful in his shirt at the end of each day.

Early remembered that missus liked flowers and that even though Aubrey said he wasn't going to be husband number three, he was always bringing black-eyed Susans he cut from along his fence out front over to the old woman.

Or was that Chub bringing daisies to Toby?

Best thing about working in the fields? Early was so tired at the end of the day, maybe he forgot to take his clothes off before he fell asleep. But sometimes, not tired enough to make sleep put quiet all the talking and whispering and crying in that place, some outside, some inside. What if D Jay came by and asked boy, what you do to get yourself in here? Maybe he'd even send over a buddy like Mr. Navy. That's when Early worked his fingers into the tiny hole in the corner of his pillow and pulled chicken feathers out one by one until he fell asleep and in the morning, hid them in an empty match box, there in the pipes going up to the ceiling, beside his bed.

They met in the lunch room with the oil stove and tiles halfway up the walls. Sometimes the windows were open and the ocean rushed in right over you, all cool and wet and salty. Most times, though, the windows were closed and the hall stunk of boiled cabbage. The other men with white letters on their backs that Early couldn't read stared through their cigarette smoke.

"Almost missed my bus."

Aubrey took off his coat and hat. The chair squeaked against the floor as he pulled it out, took a seat with his back to the stove. Bones need to keep warm, he said. Then Aubrey rubbed his leg, just above the wooden part.

"Sorry I haven't come to see you, Early. Been hard for me, you know, after Toby. What they said you did."

"We goin' home today?"

"Not today."

Aubrey got a smile that didn't make him look too happy.

"Who's gonna carry him?"

"What did you say?"

"Toby. Who's gonna carry him?"

Aubrey asked if Early remembered anything else about Toby.

Sure. Lots of things, like piggybacks to the dump, that raft of theirs—think it's okay till I get back?—going down Uncle Laffy's Hill and eating blueberries and Toby getting sick and Chub holding him in the water and Toby saying don't let me up.

"How come he doesn't come by? They don't let him in here? Or girls like Chub?"

"Early, Chub must be a young lady now."

"Yeah?"

"You know how long you've been here?"

"A long time."

Aubrey said Chub hadn't come 'round since Toby got sick, not that there was anything to come around to. After the bridge crossed the Narrows, it needed roads. One of them went through those houses on the hill where Chub lived. She and that family of hers had to move away.

"Gone?"

"Everything's gone. Missus moved. House knocked down. Church bulldozed in the middle of the night. Big Town's gone, Early, and soon, they'll tear this place down."

Even Miss Portia, God bless her, had died.

Aubrey said it was a hard day the city tore down his house and Mrs. Aada's, hearing the glass breaking in Jubilee Hall. Tractor took a few minutes to do all three. Moved Aubrey out same as Mrs. Jensen, back of a dump truck.

"Good thing too, 'cause that bridge coming across the harbour wasn't waiting. Just look up and see it. But they haven't built anything down there yet like the city said they needed Africville for."

Mrs. Aada got herself into Mulgrave Park. No room for a flower patch and all she could see out her window was a parking lot. Aubrey visited when he could, but it was hard with that leg of his.

Mrs. Trilby?

Sold. Sure. To a better place.

Aubrey had a room now on Brunswick Street. Cats messed in the hallway. Young men in the neighbourhood fought lots, and they weren't very respectful to an old man with a wooden leg that couldn't walk so fast. But Early wasn't to worry, it wouldn't be for long. He was on a list to get a place in Uniacke Square, though Aubrey couldn't say how he'd afford the rent. The city paid him one thousand dollars for his house, said they were being real generous, Mr. Daye, because Mrs. Aada owned the land, and Aubrey had to spend most of that getting Toby settled in the ground, same as D Jay. What was left over, Deborah took. Her man, Knowl, was in jail somewhere in British Columbia, last Aubrey heard, and since Aubrey had no more money, Deborah didn't bother coming 'round.

"You're looking thin, Early. You not eating?"

Not much, not since two others started working in the fields with him. Like Charlie and Tom, but not quite. Bigger, older. They told Early he was planting right on top of those prisoners that mess about and get buried alive. So when Early pulled the potatoes out of the ground, out popped their screaming mouths, maybe an eyeball too. Couldn't eat potatoes with someone's mouth attached.

Aubrey got up with his hat.

"They tell me you're moving to New Brunswick. It was good of them to keep you here as long as they could. Goodbye, Early."

Aubrey put on his coat.

"Here, don't let them see you take this."

He slid a Cherry Blossom into Early's pocket.

Early felt the afternoon sun warm against his face as he tried to hold onto the memory of Aubrey sitting at the table with him. Sometimes he did that with Toby, but he'd tried to hold onto that memory so often it was starting to get worn out and he was afraid he might lose it. Then he opened his eyes to the orange and red in the trees. The sea was nowhere in sight behind the stone building, but you sure could smell salt air and taste it if you'd a mind to stick out your tongue.

Two others were in the fields. They laughed seeing Early come with his rake, saying how do.

Retard.

That's him, that's the one that pisses himself, said the man who reminded Early of Charlie. Ha ha.

They laughed and joked with Early, jostling him about, until the three of them were alone behind that stone shed.

Early thought it was a game when they took hold of his arms. He grinned until one of the men shoved him against the wall and his head went *kerr-ack*. That's for drowning the boy, they said. Early slumped to his knees under a canopy of yellow maple.

But hurt didn't stay long in Early's head. Not with lupins sprouting through train tracks, ducks settling on the pond, and ahead, a muddy road crossed by long shadows.

INTERVIEW WITH
STEPHENS GERARD MALONE

1) WHAT DOES YOUR TYPICAL WRITING PROCESS LOOK LIKE?

The act of writing for me is like sculpting in clay, best done early in the morning. I take lots and lots of words, piled together in a rather loose kind of order. Then there's kneading and shaping, pinching, cutting, ripping off whole chunks, and then adding more words, delicately moulding the details. After one hundred pages of manuscript, I'm allowed to call it a novel, and I always like to start off by naming the book something, although it will undoubtedly go through many title changes. Generally I do three revisions before I show the manuscript to someone who can give me a challenging critique, but each one of those revisions can have countless versions.

2) WHAT ARE SOME OF YOUR FAVOURITE BOOKS? FAVOURITE WRITERS?

Blindness by José Saramago and *One Hundred Years of Solitude* by Gabriel Garcia Marquez taught me reams about writing. The Brontes, Dickens, Tolstoy, and Fitzgerald can still spellbind. Ann Fairbairn's *Five Smooth Stones*, set against the civil rights movement in the United States, was way ahead of its time and is still a damn good read. That book showed me the relevance of fiction apart from entertainment. It's a shame this once popular novel has all but disappeared.

3) What made you decide to write about such an emotionally charged issue as Africville? Was this a difficult book to write?

There was something poetic about the name Africville, and of a community that no longer existed, that captured my imagination when I moved to Nova Scotia. At the time, when I asked friends about the place, no one could describe it as anything other than a former black slum on the north end of the Halifax peninsula. But as a reader and a writer, I value the sense of place in literature, and here was a unique story of a community beloved by many and embarrassing to others. It was also a story that dealt with one of my worst fears, that of the State arbitrarily dictating how people should live. How could any writer resist such a fertile subject?

As for it being a tough book to write, I was sure it would never find an audience. I initially wrote the first of three distinct versions over six years ago. It didn't work for reasons of voice. Subsequent versions of the book were told from Chub's point of view, and then from the point of view of her Aunt Joy. Each attempt felt like the project was spinning out of control. It took sticking the manuscript in a box for years, then a fresh pair of eyes and a lot of spit and polish, to finally get it right.

4) You're a white writer writing about a community of black or, to borrow George Elliot Clarke's term, Africadian, people. Does this matter to you? Was it something you considered when you set out to write the novel?

As a writer, I'm fascinated by the motivations behind the politically incorrect side of the story. My first novel, *Endless Bay*, was told in first person, from the point of view of a woman who victimized her native lover. I had to submit it under a pseudonym to even get a publisher to read it. *I Still*

Have a Suitcase in Berlin was told from the perspective of a Nazi sympathizer. So no, when I began writing the novel, it didn't matter to me that I was white, writing about a black community. It challenged me. If anything, the subject dared me. I *made* race matter when I couldn't get the early versions of the book to work because I needed a crutch to explain my failure; I could not write about Africville because it's not my story to tell. After the book found a home, the crutch had to go and with it, my belief that the novel was a story about a black community. It's really about racism. And that story is mine to tell.

5) The community of Africville, as you've portrayed it in the novel, has its share of problems. What are the issues, as you see them, in portraying a community's negative aspects?

Any portrayal of Africville is complicated by decades of bad feelings over the forced relocation, and that many of the residents are still alive. I had to ignore that or I never would have written the book. For me, there must be a disconnect between what goes on the page and how I think the reader will respond. Taboo gets put outside the door. I need free rein to visit any dark place a story takes me. However, while I'm not a journalist, I do believe that fiction needs truthfulness of context, and the story should have social relevance. But as to how much dirty laundry to hang out for all to see, and how graphically to illustrate it, I think that depends on the style of narrative and character development. In *Big Town*, the reader needed to know certain elements about the inhabitants' background, and the conditions in Africville, presented in a way that was faithful to how Early saw things.

Even so, some may argue that my depiction is like peeling a scab off an old wound. Others may wonder, why revisit this painful period in our past? That debate is for the reader, and not this writer.

6) The action in *Big Town* comes to us via Early's point of view, yet he repeatedly admits to being "not good at remembering things." Why did you decide to write the novel from his point of view?

Initially, I didn't. Early was a minor character at the outset modelled after a dog. Even though he rarely spoke in that first draft, his voice was the loudest. There was something about his faithfulness, his innocence, his non-judgmental way that made me realize his was the voice I needed between the two polarities of this story—although Early's lack of credibility forces the reader to think twice about what really happened. Early also provided a certain amount of authenticity. Telling the story from his perspective, that of an outsider to the community and to its demise, paralleled my own much-removed experience with Africville.

7) Can you explain the significance of the title?

The novel, until publication, was called *Africville*. But that title always felt more obvious than natural, especially with Early's unique voice. I first came across the name in Charles R. Saunders' recollections in *The Spirit of Africville* where he describes Big Town as that part of the community when coming in from Barrington Street as "lookin' like raisins on a layer cake." In the novel, Africville may have been the home to Toby and his family, but it was a town big enough to be Early's entire world.

8) **Early, Toby, and Chub, the main characters in the book, are all children. Why did you decide to present the novel through the eyes of children?**

Because *Big Town* is first and foremost, a story of racism, and children are the future, presenting the novel through the eyes of children lets me show how they are taught to hate, often in subtle ways, and then to pay it forward. Chub and Toby's natural inclinations towards each other are coloured by the conditioning of their families. Chub, especially, parrots sentiments she has no understanding of. And because children's memories are imperfect and their understanding of things incomplete, viewing the community through their eyes allowed me to interject a tinge of whimsy as relief from passages of abuse and neglect.

9) **For readers who aren't familiar with the history of Africville, what is the legacy of that place today?**

After four decades the City of Halifax apologized to the former residents. The church is to be rebuilt in situ as a museum and interpretive centre. Seaview Park has been renamed back to Africville. It that enough? Only the former residents can say. It was their homes that were bulldozed during the night. But perhaps the lasting legacy of Africville lies in the walls still dividing this city, suggesting that the bitter taste of racism, particularly the kind practiced as a matter of government policy, can outlast any act of contrition.

For a Big Town reading group guide, please visit nimbus.ca and search "Big Town" or send an email to: customerservice@nimbus.ca

STEPHENS GERARD MALONE IS THE AUTHOR OF
I Still Have a Suitcase in Berlin, Endless Bay, and
Miss Elva, which was shortlisted for the Dartmouth Book
Award. He lives in Halifax.
Visit him at: stephensgerardmalone.wordpress.com

Careers for You Series

CAREERS FOR

COMPUTER BUFFS

& Other Technological Types

MAJORIE EBERTS
MARGARET GISLER

THIRD EDITION

McGraw·Hill

New York   Chicago   San Francisco   Lisbon   London   Madrid   Mexico City
Milan   New Delhi   San Juan   Seoul   Singapore   Sydney   Toronto

Library of Congress Cataloging-in-Publication Data

Eberts, Marjorie.
    Careers for computer buffs & other technological types / Marjorie Eberts,
Margaret Gisler.— 3rd ed.
        p.   cm. — (McGraw-Hill careers for you series)
       ISBN 0-07-145877-8 (alk. paper)
        1. Computer science—Vocational guidance.   2. Electronic data processing—
Vocational guidance.   I. Gisler, Margaret.   II. Title.

QA76.25.E23 2006
004′.023—dc22   2005024056

*To Jim Horio, an outstanding computer
expert and director of information
technology extraordinaire. You are
a true and helpful friend.*

1 2 3 4 5 6 7 8 9 0   DOC/DOC   0 9 8 7 6

ISBN 0-07-145877-8

McGraw-Hill books are available at special quantity discounts to use as premiums and
sales promotions, or for use in corporate training programs. For more information,
please write to the Director of Special Sales, Professional Publishing, McGraw-Hill,
Two Penn Plaza, New York, NY 10121-2298. Or contact your local bookstore.

This book is printed on acid-free paper.

Contents